PRAIRIE WINGS

TO E. S. Q.

Prairie Wings   *Richard E. Bishop*

"Thou rang'd and cloud cleaving ministers
Whose happy flight is highest into heaven.
Thee art gone where the eye cannot follow thee.
But thine yet pierces downward, onward, or above
With a pervading vision......"

"*Thou winged and cloud cleaving ministers*
Whose happy flight is highest into heaven,
Thee art gone where the eye cannot follow thee.
But thine yet pierces downward, onward, or above
With a pervading vision. . . . . ."

PRAIRIE WINGS

Pen and Camera Flight Studies

by

EDGAR M. QUEENY

Explanatory Sketches by

RICHARD E. BISHOP

J. B. LIPPINCOTT COMPANY

Philadelphia and New York

1947

Contents

Illustrations

Preface

Evening flight

MIGRATORY *birds are true internationalists. They are citizens of our continent; the whole of it is their home. As the web-footed subjects appearing in this volume passed through Arkansas, no one could have identified the region whence any one of them came. Some originated in the marshes along Alaska's Yukon, some in the prairies of Saskatchewan, some in the barren wastes surrounding Hudson Bay. One could be certain only that the ponds in which they swam as ducklings were turned into ice and that their nesting grasses lay deep under snow. A few of them flew on to Mexico. Most halted at the Gulf Coast, lodging there for the winter. The rest awaited spring in Arkansas, feeding in its rice fields and sheltering in its pin oak flats. But whether enroute to more southerly parts or as winter residents of Arkansas, their stay there forms the topic of this book.*

Because of the mechanical and chemical limitations of lens and film, the means of presenting flight photographically is still unequal to the beauty of birds and the easy grace with which flight is performed. Nor is photography yet able to capture the cold, pale hues of dawn, the first faint highlights and shadows of day, or the crystal aroma of the silent marsh and fenlands, which, as much as the quarry itself, form irresistible lures which draw gunnermen to be their witnesses.

Nevertheless, photography is able to detect action that escapes the most intent eye; and by recording positions taken in the slightest instants, we are helped to understand flight and the gravity-defying instruments of flight, Nature's most wondrous evolution—the wings of birds.

Richard E. Bishop, who has spent a lifetime absorbing the theme of flight, not only gave these pages his friendly, careful criticism but made so many helpful suggestions that I requested him to appear as co-author. He graciously declined. I am certain, however, that readers will agree that his painting, "Prairie Wings," reproduced as the frontispiece, and his decorative and interpretive sketches and comment supply the all-necessary leaven to this loaf.

These pages have also benefited from a perusal of them by Dr. Rudolf Bennitt, of Missouri University's Department of Zoology; Charles W. Schwartz, project leader, Missouri Conservation Commission; and Ray E. Benson, of Ducks Unlimited's staff.

Glenn L. Martin's interest in waterfowl yields precedence only to his interest in aircraft. He is my fellow trustee of Ducks Unlimited, and its active, diligent vice-president. Many, many thousand geese winter in sanctuaries he maintains for them near Baltimore. There he observes their habits and flight; he photographs them, also.

Together with the able engineers associated with him, Glenn Martin, too, reviewed this book. Many helpful suggestions resulted, especially regarding the chapters dealing with flight. And for the inquiring mind, Mr. Martin contributed the pertinent engineering discussion of bird flight appearing in the Addenda.

C. Townsend Ludington, associate director of Philadelphia's Franklin Institute, cooperated by examining the chapter, "Instruments of Flight," in which I quote from his illuminating book, Smoke Streams. He graciously permitted reproduction of his illustrations visualizing air flow, which aided greatly in placing the ramifying subject of flight in what I hope will prove an understandable form.

My appreciation is also due George P. Vierheller, director of the St. Louis Zoological Garden, who gave me specimens from which my wing and feather studies were made; to Dr. Gordon L. Walls, for reviewing the comments on duck vision appearing in the Addenda; to Mrs. George W. Wilcox, for permission to reproduce the extraordinary photographs of massed ducks on Wilcox Lake, one of which forms the end sheets; and to the Arkansas Game and Fish Commission, for permission to use the exceptional photograph of a White River concentration.

And both Mr. Bishop and I are happy to acknowledge the great debt which we owe to Ducks Unlimited, for their contributions to our increased wildfowl population.

EDGAR M. QUEENY
Wingmead, Roe, Arkansas

Chapter One _____

BETWEEN-SEASON NOSTALGIA

Dropping in

WHEN the sands of his life were running low and his eyesight was failing, Viscount Grey returned to the solace of the rustic towers and musty books of his beloved Fallodon. There, in a detached and reminiscent mood, he rummaged in the garret of his mind. Turning over and re-examining events of the years that had piled one upon another while he was young, active, and a world personality, he searched them for wisdom. He mused. He ruminated. Fortunately for us, he revealed and preserved his conclusions in some charming essays.

In one of them, while penetrating the subject of the precise nature of happiness, he observed that any event giving real pleasure is thrice enjoyed! There is the pleasure of anticipation, he pointed out, then the pleasure of realization, and finally the third pleasure of retrospection.

But when Grey dipped his pen into the memories of events providing him these pleasures, he wrote not of palace garden parties, nor of his political successes, nor of his diplomatic achievements. His pen was wet with memories of simple ventures with nature. He recalled the pleasures of excursions to trout streams and sallies into the woodlands. Knowing the life and habits of salmon and trout, Viscount Grey enjoyed outwitting them. He also absorbed to the full the lives of British birds. It might be said with truth that he lived Longfellow's phrases, because he

> "Learned of every bird its language,
>
> Learned their names and all their secrets,
>
> How they built their nests in Summer,
>
> Where they hid themselves in Winter,
>
> Talked with them whene'er he met them."

And now he enjoyed these pleasures in retrospect.

Such were the subjects of his essays and so did he answer the question—What are the real pleasures of life?

Events of the same nature that gave Grey his true pleasures have provided me with mine. I have followed his example of using leisure moments to recall them, meditate upon them, and re-enjoy them. I have found, too, that it is a good exercise to reduce thoughts to written words because it unveils them to one's self. Voids are then apparent which, after study and inquiry, may be filled in. Inconsistencies, obscured in the mind by the rapid flow of thought, glare back from written words and cry out for correction until orderly form prevails.

And as one can escape from today's chaos of ugly humors and enjoy an evening by reading a book, absorbing and digesting ideas from its type, so, too, an escape is provided by an evening spent in reversing this process and conveying one's own recollections and reflections to paper, shaping them in written words. Therefore, I have indulged in this volume, portraying with pen and photographs some of the pleasures and their by-products that I have derived from the flight of ducks.

Most of the photographs were made in a pin oak flat on Arkansas' Grand Prairie, and when leafing them over I recall the days I have passed within its reaches. The most pleasant were spent in good company when friends and retrievers shared plenteous activities. However, with gun or camera in hand, I have passed day after day in a blind alone. Usually I kept busy watching flights scudding over the tree tops, hoping my decoys and call would lure them. Sometimes, however, ducks were not flying or they preferred using other parts of the flat. At such times I was left amid its vast silence to muse on the enigmas of human existence and the bewitching mysteries of nature.

P. D. Ouspensky, the Russian mystic and philosopher, maintains that one's consciousness enters the world of noumena when one can hear the voice of a silence. He adds that there are many silences and many inanimate voices. By way of illustration, he points out that the silence of a prison cell differs from the silence of an empty church.

Certainly, then, there is a difference between the silence of a prison cell and the silence of a forest. If in a prison cell one can hear the grim voices of blocks of stone and iron bars, then in the forest one can hear the genial voices of trees.

Probably our generation will never know whether stone and other members of the mineral kingdom, or trees and other members of the vegetable kingdom, possess voices. But, in the silence of nature, there is something that transcends the apprehension of our mortal senses. Whatever it, or they, may be—let us call them voices—they haunt our souls and make truants of our minds, which escape from the labyrinth of things as they are and wander in the transfinite world of noumena or in fairylands of things as we wish them to be.

There *are* differences in the nuances and timbres of nature's voices, too! In the hollow of an icy fiord, for instance, who can be unaware of the engulfing muteness of its stentorian granite walls? And on the edge of the Colorado's Grand Canyon, cannot one hear the chorus of vibrant awe welling up from its dead millenniums? Who can look at the galaxy of embers in night's open firmament and not hear voiced in the glow his own insignificance? And who can escape wondering as to the nature of the everlasting, as dawn, the eternal fugitive from sunrise, silently extinguishes stars and calls man back from dreams into being?

These silences differ in tone-color and emotions evoked, as much as the music of one type of instrument differs from that of another, or the music of one nation differs from that of another.

Even the tone of a forest's silence changes. After it has been interrupted by the fall of one of its old monarchs, after the crackling as his branches tangled and tore away those of other trees, and after the hollow "boom" has died away, there is a more absolute, more omnipresent silence as the last sprays of twigs and leaves drift down.

And, further, the gay silence of the woods in sunlight is different from the eerie hush that is the deep silence of its night. Then, perhaps, with their leaves curled, the trees are asleep and the only voice is that of some dying embers of a campfire, at whose call "memories come drifting back like cows to a barn in the evening"—memories of the cracked marl of the Saskatchewan prairies from which arose the flying wedge of ducks we had glimpsed that evening; memories of a covey of bobwhites that erupted out of the sedge grass beneath our feet, and of the erect head and tousled, silken ears of the setter that held his point; memories of paddles dipping gently into water, the pristine stream beyond the marks of man, the wild, wild cry of the loon!

There are silent voices of animals, too, such as that of the dog which nudges his moist nose and sleek head under one's arm and with pleading eyes asks for a friendly pat, then silently voices his gratitude by wagging his tail.

Grey Owl, the pseudo half-breed chronicler of the northland, believed that the Indian's attitude toward nature was summed up in a casual remark made by an old Ojibway companion. One night when the red man sat motionless as a bronze statue, his face lighted by a flickering campfire, he observed, "When the wind speaks to the leaves, the Indian hears—and understands."

And, fortunately for us, when the voice of the wind spoke to the leaves, such men as Audubon, John Muir, Frederick Remington, W. H. Hudson, and Viscount Grey also heard, understood, and recorded, for our everlasting enjoyment.

It was the voices of the wind and nature's wild kingdoms which lured Francis Parkman to the Oregon Trail when a white man was still an alien in that region. There he "struggled through copses and lines of wood, waded brooks and pools of water, traversed prairie as green as an emerald, expanding mile after mile wilder and more wild than the waste Mazeppa rode over, where neither

> .... Man nor brute
> Nor dent of hoof, nor print of foot,
> Lay in the wild luxuriant soil—
> No sign of travel, none of toil—
> The very air was mute."

All animals, all vegetables, and all minerals, the trinity of nature's kingdoms, have one common ancestor—the whirling nebula of fire and light that split off, sought its own orbit, then burned itself out to become the aggregate of astral ash which is our planet. And man and dog had a more recent common ancestor in the bit of animate organized matter that made up the first slimy, single-celled creature.

All matter, modern physics teaches, is merely congealed energy or light. The true elements of man, tree, and stone are tiny charges of electric energy: electrons, protons, neutrons. They are common to all kingdoms.

In children's stories and in the mythology of primitive peoples, this kinship is recognized. In such tales, there is no differentiation in the existence of man, tree, and stone. All are animated, all have personalities. Tree and stone, as well as man, think, speak, and act. Even such phenomena as thunder and tempests are endowed with personalities, temperaments, and human affections, good or evil. In legends, men speak to animals and animals to trees. There are reversible metamorphoses. The mythological figure Hiawatha, for instance, who deemed himself related to all animals, changed himself at will into a tree and back into a man. The Mewan Indians believed that the First People to inhabit our world were transformed into trees, rocks, animals, celestial bodies, hail, and rain; and that the Indians themselves descended from feathers which the First People planted in the ground. According to Homer, the rock Scylla was an evil, plotting female. And in Grimm's Tales a prince is transformed into a frog; his plight seems not unnatural to children.

In spite of the fences shutting us within our sedentary, materialistic adult lives, an instinctive mysticism and some childlike sentiments still linger in our emotional natures. And at times we are conscious of the voices of our elemental kin. For each of us, there are voices from one or more of nature's moods with which he is in especial harmony. Sometimes they call loudly and persistently. And in addition to their nigh-irresistible call, there is the cogent council of the Indians' Great Spirit—

"Drudge not, grind not, White Man, for thy pence,

Merely to store thy purses with their shining poison."

So, with a rod, one may answer the call of a distant stream, stand in its foamy rapids, and drop a fly into its deep, dark pools. Another, with a willing dog to search out its hedgerows, answers the field. Still another responds by wandering in a forest whose trunks, limbs, and leaves form the pillars, the arches, and the flecked dome of a natural cathedral wherein, with the sweet smell of moss and leaf mold as incense, he may lose himself in soul-searching communion.

And in those of us who derive enjoyment from the flight of wildfowl and who know Arkansas' Grand Prairie, a wistful nostalgia for its pin oak flats simmers and simmers throughout spring and summer months. It boils over when the first yellow leaf of autumn whispers that the Hunting Winds are on their way. And when the woodlands along the White River are ablaze with red and orange tints and the air tastes tangy with frost, the call of the Prairie and its denizens is insistent, siren-like—almost hypnotic.

There is only one antidote—to respond!

Fall habitant of the Grand Prairie

A million wings rise above the White River

Chapter Two

THE GRAND PRAIRIE

Early visitor

THE Grand Prairie of Arkansas presents an historical paradox. This region, one of the first areas in the United States to come under a white man's eye, remained one of the last whose soil was broken by his plow. Sixty years before the *Susan Constance,* the *Godspeed,* and the *Discovery* furled their sails and dropped anchor in the James River, and Chief Powhatan saw the first permanent English settlers step onto American soil, Hernandez De Soto sought an El Dorado or the South Sea in the Middle West. He started inland from the Gulf Coast with six hundred and twenty picked men. In the vanguard were his caballeros, wearing shining breastplates, lances in hand, mounted on armored, copper-shod horses. Bright blades of Toledo steel hung at their sides. His infanteria, bearing heavy cross-bows, followed afoot. Then came priests and monks, to save the Indians' souls.

After cutting his way to the Tennessee River, De Soto turned southwest until he came upon a "Rio Grande"—the Mississippi. He crossed, set foot on its western bank near what is now Helena, then climbed up Crowley's Ridge. Upon this vantage point the Spaniard stood in his stirrups, pushed back his sallet, and, shielding his eyes from the setting sun, looked out upon the limitless verdure of the Grand Prairie. It beckoned him on. So he waved his men forward.

Descending the ridge's western slope, he crossed the broad plain, forded the White River, and forced a way through the densely timbered wilderness to the west. When he reached the neighborhood of Little Rock's present site, he encamped for the winter. With the arrival of spring, the Ouachita River rose in full spate; so, embarking his men and horses on rafts, he trusted to its waters in hopes of regaining the Mississippi. He died enroute. But the remnant of his troop, scarcely three hundred men, kept on until they reached the Gulf, then turned toward Mexico and their compatriots.

One hundred and forty-one years later, as Charles II was signing a charter granting William Penn a refuge for persecuted Quakers, Sieur de LaSalle, who was descending the Mississippi, spied the wide mouth of the Arkansas River. Pulling his pirogues up on its banks, he planted the banner of His Most Christian Majesty, Louis XIV, and took possession of the territory in his name. Then he resumed his journey.

Later, Henri de Tonti, LaSalle's lieutenant who had become separated from his chief, touched shore at the same inviting spot. He, however, poled up the Arkansas' winding course for some sixty miles, then landed. The Quapaw Indians, who greeted de Tonti and his voyageurs, were hospitable. Some of the voyageurs liked them and were attracted by the abundance of game and prospects of establishing trade. They secured permission to remain and established the first white settlement on the lower Mississippi, Arkansas Post.

Even after another century had passed and the colonies of Penn and John Smith had joined with eleven others to secure their independence and become a nation, there were scarcely three hundred white men in the vast expanse known as The Territory of the Arkansas. Largely unknown and unexplored, it stretched south and west till its undefined boundaries shaded into those of Mexico. To the north lay another wilderness, The Territory of the Missouri.

But this handful of Frenchmen had penetrated much of Arkansas; they left marks enduring to this day. As they hunted, trapped, and traded all over the Grand Prairie, many of its towns, watercourses, and families still bear French names.

The Grand Prairie is an elongated, inverted, trapezoidal area whose narrow base begins below Cape Girardeau, Missouri. Nesting between the foothills of the Ozark Mountains on the west and Crowley's Ridge on the east, it reaches south till its apex merges into the flood plain below Arkansas Post, where the Arkansas joins the Mississippi. To one's eye, the Prairie seems to stretch into eternity in all directions. It is broken, however, by the White River as it twists its way to join the Arkansas almost at its junction with the Mississippi. Emptying into the White River are numerous bayous that have cut meandering courses through the Prairie's smooth fields.

Tall savannas of hickory, sweet gum, water oak, and pin oak line the banks of the bayous and spread over the frequent low flatlands which creep away from the watercourses with an almost imperceptible rise. These flats are usually flooded in spring and fall, when heavy rains send the bayous' tawny waters out of their banks to cover the surrounding carpets of leaves.

Forty years ago the Prairie's soil was still unbroken. Arkansas was settled by cotton farmers from Mississippi, Alabama, Georgia, and other states of the deep south, but these pioneers found the Prairie unsuited to a cotton crop, so moved on and staked out farther west. The Grand Prairie was left unclaimed; homestead land was still available, practically for the asking, at the turn of the century. The relatively few who settled there used the Prairie as an open cattle range.

So it remained an island of virgin country in the center of a rapidly growing agricultural and industrial nation. And by this accident it retained its wildlife. Until quite recently the Prairie teemed with prairie chickens. Deer, bear, and wild turkeys abounded in the woods, along the bayous, and in the overflow land along the White River. Small fur-bearing animals and quail were everywhere.

Now, unfortunately, prairie chickens have been exterminated. But quail and small fur-bearers still thrive. In sadly diminished numbers, other wildlife has sought refuge in the overflow. The knell was sounded in 1904, when a field near Carlisle was planted to rice and a phenomenal harvest was reaped.

Rice must be grown in water. Farmers soon learned that a hardpan underlying the topsoil in this area held water like a saucer, and that there was an ample water supply near the surface that could be pumped to flood the fields. Fifteen years later, several hundred thousand acres of the Grand Prairie's virgin soil had been turned under and millions of bushels of rice were being harvested annually. The Prairie had become one of the world's important rice-producing areas. Although oats, lespedeza, and soybeans are often grown in rotation with rice, and cattle do well also, rice remains the principal crop of the Prairie.

There is still some of the Prairie that has never known a plow. It is good pasture; its grass makes good hay. This virgin soil is studded occasionally with small mounds covered with clumps of trees. Natives call them "gas boils." Then one is reminded that not long ago, as geological time goes, the Mississippi's ancestor swept through the area. Later on, torrents from the melting glaciers farther north flooded it, depositing the sand and gravel rived from northern stone. Irrigation water is now pumped from this stratum. As the glacial water's velocity decreased, the deposit became finer and finer, until the present soils were built. Geologists believe that the mounds resulted from water spouts as the subsidence of top soils compressed subsurface water. In escaping, it formed vents and carried up with it the sand and soil now forming the mounds.

Most of the Prairie's roads and some of its fields are lined with tangled hedges of sumac, honeysuckle, trumpet vine, wild plum, or blackberry, interspersed now and then with a cluster of red haw or sassafras. Here and there a persimmon, honey locust, or Osage orange tops the row. In late fall, there is evidence under every persimmon tree that opossums have been enjoying its fruit, "possum apples." Bobwhites nest in this excellent cover and in the thickets and broom sedge of such adjoining fields as lie fallow.

Along these roadsides are frequent cottages nestling in groves of trees, usually post oaks. But here and there one finds ash or pecan trees, evergreen cedars, luxuriant lilac and chinaberry bushes, or tall, beautifully polished, waxen-leaved hollies. Some of the cottages are white and from a distance may remind one of those on Cape Cod; but most are unpainted, unkempt, and weather-beaten. Each, however, has its red brick chimney from which, in winter, pungent wood smoke is ever rising and tilting or bending with the breeze. Most cottages are stuffed to overflowing with Negro families. In such cases cotton patches are always near by. Pickaninnies are sprawled on the porches and the door frames are filled with bright calico dresses or blue denim overalls, each topped by a smiling black face which greets passers-by with a nod and a friendly "How's y'awl dis mawnin'?"

By November, rice has been harvested and stubble fields are dry, presenting the drab and somber appearance of freshly cut-over wheat fields which have been fluted by a multitude of small, rib-like levees following the land's contours. The stubble is strewn with rice kernels that have shattered off during harvest, providing a bountiful food supply not only for quail, doves, and other birds of the local habitat but for the millions of migrants which pour through the Prairie in winter.

During the southern migration, ducks feed in these rice fields at night. By day they rest and sip in the shallow, placid, densely wooded waters of the flats. There one hears them gabbling and chuckling as they dive occasionally for the pin oak acorns that have fallen to the bottom. Late flights—the big so-called "redlegs" and "ice mallards"—end their migration there, passing the winter with diurnal flights between rice fields and flats. In February they depart for their northern breeding grounds.

The great Mississippi flyway is shaped like a funnel. Along the Grand Prairie it narrows into the tube. Officials of the United States Fish and Wildlife Service estimate that forty to fifty per cent of all North America's wildfowl use the Mississippi flyway and pass through this tube. Most of this great number pour out of its mouth upon the Mississippi delta and spread over the marshes of the Gulf Coast. The remainder winter in Arkansas.

Because all watercourses within the mountain ranges of our continent's east and west coasts have beckoned them to the Mississippi, geese from bleak and far-eastern Baffin Land and mallards, greenwings, and pintails from the barren wastes of the upper Yukon join their relatives from the Prairie provinces in Arkansas. Ducks from Hudson Bay's eastern shores pass over Lake St. Clair, then trace the Ohio River to its junction with the Mississippi; those from Manitoba follow the Illinois, the Sangamon, and the Wabash to the Mississippi; those from Western Arctic tundras, lured by promises of sheltered backwaters and bountiful food, follow the courses of the Missouri, the Platte, the White, the Arkansas, and the great Father of Waters itself. During migrations all these flights meet and linger in the flats of Arkansas' Grand Prairie, composing the world's greatest concentration of wildfowl.

In number, mallards dwarf all other species of the flyway. But all North American river ducks, or Anatinae, are represented, as well as a few diving ducks with lobed hind toes, such as ringnecks, lesser scaups, and an occasional redhead.

The Grand Prairie is neither a lush nor an awesome region. A productive agricultural area seldom is. But in spring and fall it exhibits some beautiful moods. November's mood has great charm.

Standing on the edge of a pin oak flat at dawn of a typical November day in air that is chill, damp, and sweet, one sees the tree tops only in shadowy outline against a slate-colored sky. Early flights of ducks are scudding over the Prairie like low, dark, storm-borne, serpentine clouds, undulating, twisting, and weaving as they form, break, and re-form into varying elongated shapes. Flight after flight

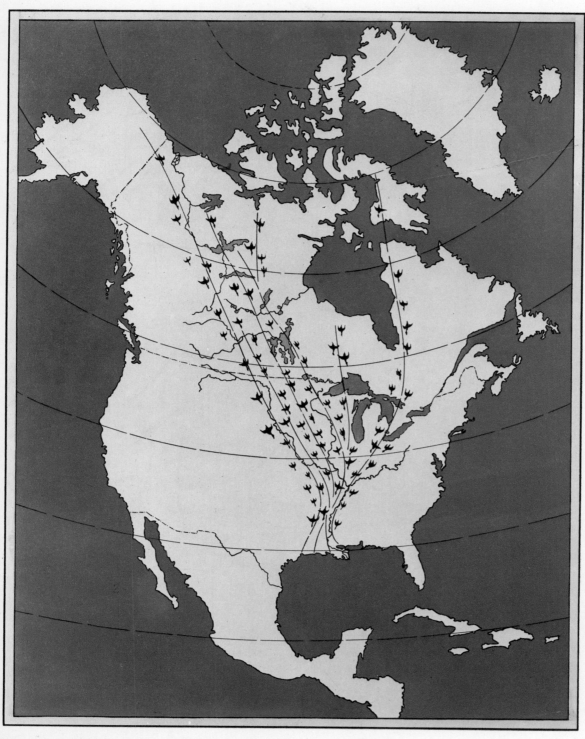

The funnel-shaped Mississippi flyway converges in Arkansas
(Drawn by C. L. Russell from Circular 342, U. S. Department of Agriculture)

passes overhead, then cruises over the flat and deploys for reconnaissance. The silhouettes of single birds are barely distinguishable against the sky, but one hears distinctly the swishing of air through flight feathers and the gabbling—talk and back-talk—as merits of various patches of sheltered waters are discussed. Then, like those that have passed over before, each flight vanishes into the mass of trees.

The sky pales, then reddens, as the sun rises above the horizon and lights the tree tops. Golden leaves of hickory and pin oak and stained crimson leaves of sweet gum glisten in bold contrast to the somber browns and greys of the branches. And the depths beneath this canopy are veiled by a curtain of purple mist lifting slowly from the water. At tree-top height it dissolves into the sunbeams. Thin wafers of crisp rime mark the edges of the flat.

Within an hour or two it is warm and clear. Rime and frost have melted; the sky is a deep blue. Billowing wool packs drift slowly toward the east. And for several hours after sunrise, flights of drowsy ducks which linger in the rice fields are stirred by either man or sun; on lazy wings they seek a haven in the flats.

Woodpeckers are on the go constantly. Their short, eccentric flights from tree to tree are followed by staccato hammerings against the trunks. Some are the large, pileated variety—"Good Gods" the natives call them. Often a fox squirrel runs down a limb, jumps to another, and barks in loud disproportion to his tiny size. Occasionally a blue heron or sand hill crane, flopping huge wings, floats by and startles the setting with a raucous, archaic cry.

Had the Mandan Indians lived in the Grand Prairie, they would have named November's moon their Moon of Falling Leaves instead of their Moon of Snowshoes, for in Arkansas November not only provides the color and climate of early October along the Platte, but toward November's end, whenever a breeze rustles through the flats, withered leaves part from their twigs and drift down to the accompaniment of acorns pattering into the water. On its tawny surface, the leaves form tight, alluring mats of spotted color. And as the boughs are laid bare, clusters of mistletoe make their appearance.

November's sunset and twilight are usually November's dawn and sunrise reversing themselves in the west. Day closes as a curtain of light blue, deepening into black, follows one fading from red to yellow over the horizon. And as long as the flats remain outlined against this backdrop, one distinguishes silhouettes of ducks swarming out of their gloomy depths and stringing across the Prairie as they retrace their morning's course back to the rice fields. Even as dusk takes over, the murmuring of wings overhead betrays occasional flights of stragglers.

Whoever is unfamiliar with this region may consider words picturing prolonged swarms of ducks to be extravagant language. However, Fish and Wildlife Service officials counted 135,000 ducks on one flat of 300 acres, 500,000 on another of 640 acres, and more than 1,000,000 on a third of 1600 acres. Therefore, when a day spent in one of these flats is done, the hours of the diurnal flights, as well as those between them, have been filled with displays of two of nature's great wonders—bird flight and her bounteous production.

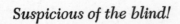

During their stay in the Prairie, these migrants feed in rice fields at night, returning at dawn to pin oak flats for rest and shelter.

Suspicious of the blind!

Above the pin oaks

Blackjacks sizzling in high octane flight

Through a tangle of branches

Resting amidst the knees and shadows of ancient cypress on Wilcox Lake. This wildfowl photograph is generally conceded to be the most extraordinary one in existence. When it was made—in 1932—wildlife authorities estimated that almost four million ducks were concentrated on this 120-acre lake.

(Courtesy Mrs. G. W. Wilcox)

(Courtesy Mrs. G. W. Wilcox)

"Up they rose with cry and clamor,
Pinions beating against the sky."

In Arkansas, small lakes along the White River's banks are trimmed with lofty, feathery Bald Cypress reaching a height of 150 feet or more. Growing in water, parts of the roots double back out of it, forming around the trunk concentric rings of uncanny, conical buttresses. These so-called "knees" act as breathing organs for the submerged roots.

page 27

Green-winged teal in quick getaway. Teal not only beat their wings rapidly but, for ducks, they have a very high ratio of wing area to body weight; hence their speed.

Gadwalls pitching

page 29

Circling

Hen or drake? This autumn spoonbill might be either! Drakes are not adorned with their nuptial plumage nor do their bills usually turn black until December.

Vigorous downbeat

Chapter Three

ASPECTS OF FLIGHT

Turning sharply to avoid a branch

To witness a flight to advantage, one should be deep in the flat and concealed in a blind. Even before the first streak of dawn, ducks start arriving; at sunrise the flight reaches its height. They appear overhead, sometimes singly, sometimes in pairs, and sometimes in swarms. On set wings they scale down to the tree tops; then with a slow wingbeat they cruise over the flat seeking a likely landing spot. One frequently notices a pendant, rice-stuffed crop looking ever so much like a telltale of a pelican misalliance in the bird's family tree.

Ducks exhibit a variety of moods when landing on these waters. Sometimes appearing apparently out of nowhere, blackjacks and teal side-slip through the branches and plunge brazenly into their landing, upturned feet pushing the water ahead like a pair of pontoons. Among mallards and pintails, however, caution prevails. After much reassuring circling, they descend slowly. If the wind is light, beating wings work against gravity. Necks and bodies are arched so that the bills are often level with the dangling feet. After hovering, they inch into the water feet first, then fold their wings with deliberation.

Possessed of a matchless sense of aerodynamic balance, ducks know wind direction unerringly even though its force may be so delicate as barely to tilt a cigarette's rising smoke. They always take advantage of its steadying force by landing into it with wings outstretched, feet extended, webs spread wide, and tail fully fanned.

Preparatory to landing, wingbeat is slowed. As speed is lost, tail and after part of the body drop from the horizontal flying position to an angle that may approach forty-five degrees. Balance is maintained by an occasional flexing of the wing wrists, fanning and twisting of the tail, movements of the lowered legs, and opening and closing of webs. Even the winglets, the small thumb feathers on the upper part of the wings, act as wing slots when raised, increasing the wings' effectiveness.

All these navigational aids are brought into play quickly when downward-scaling ducks encounter an unexpected gust or updraft, or if sudden changes in direction are necessary, as when dodging branches of trees.

If one is very fortunate, he may witness the arrival of a new flight weary from a long migration. Before his searching eyes have spotted them, they have seen and selected a patch of water for rest and recuperation. At first they appear as mere dots, then as tiny inverted anchors suspended from the sky. It seems as though, coming from another world, they have found a hole in our heavens and are pouring through it. They tumble down haphazardly and then, like dive bombers, plunge precipitously. One distinguishes cupped wings first, then craning necks and extended feet. As they near, one hears a hissing sound like escaping steam. It is air sizzling past flight feathers and spilling out of wings. Without hesitation, they swirl and funnel into an opening in the trees and, as needles to a magnet, drop quickly and quietly into the water, rafting and crowding as though surface rent were a thousand dollars an acre.

One may stand up and wave his arms, even shout, but they come on. One thousand follows another thousand down to the landing. Nothing, it appears, will thwart their determination to light and rest. It may require twenty minutes or more for a large flight to land, but silence prevails among them until all are down.

It is a never-to-be-forgotten sight.

After landing, the first thought of these migrants seems to be to quench their thirst. Dipping bills into the water, they drink heartily. Then, after a pause, the inquisitive ones paddle off on brief explorations. Others, illustrating the origin of "ducking," tip and plunge head and shoulders deep into the water, then rise as glistening beads run over their backs. Others raise themselves out of the water, erect as West Pointers on parade, and, with heads back, chests out, dry their flight feathers with accelerated waving of wings. Then, slowly slipping back, they evince their happiness with vigorous shaking of heads and merry twitching of tails. An occasional plaintive, throaty *quack* brings from answering drakes short, low-pitched, reed-like notes similar to those of a jew's-harp.

But they are exhausted. Some have lost as much as half a pound during their flight. If they become aware of an interloper, they do not fly away but swim off or make short flights over one another. This "rolling over," as Arkansas natives term it, sounds much like combers climbing and pounding on a beach.

The average length of migratory flights is unknown. Estimates vary from 200 to 600 miles. It is known that pintails and spoonbills migrate from Alaska to Hawaii over 2,200 miles of open water. Presumably they alight enroute for rest but they have no opportunity to feed.

In 1943 the Fish and Wildlife Service reported an unprecedented arrival of a flock of pintails on Palmyra Island, the home of goony birds. Palmyra is 1,100 miles south of Hawaii. It is possible this flight was made without a stop, for the naval officer who reported the arrival said these intrepid birds were so exhausted they could be caught quite readily by hand.

Altitudes of migratory flights are dependent upon weather. Dr. Alexander Wetmore believes that in clear weather heights seldom exceed 3,000 feet. He sets 5,000 feet as a probable maximum. Basing his opinion on observations made from airplanes and theodolites designed to gauge speed of airplanes, as well as timed flights over measured courses, he estimates the speed of migrating geese and ducks to be between forty-five and fifty-nine miles an hour.

Bird migration is one of nature's mysteries. Ancients believed that when summer birds disappeared, they had transmuted themselves into other birds or even animals. Gordon C. Aymar says Aristotle believed that the European robin changed into a redstart. Both Aristotle and Pliny, while evidencing some knowledge of migration, thought that most birds hibernated in winter like bears. The Mewan Indians had a better conception. They believed that the home of ducks was in the north cold country, "on the other side of the sky," the pathway to their home leading through a "north hole" in the sky which opened and closed with such rapidity that only the swiftest fliers could pass through.

What knowledge we have of migration is comparatively recent. Yet ducks that arrive in Arkansas have followed a course traveled by their ancestors when the flats' towering oaks were mere acorns, and, before them, by countless thousands of earlier generations. Many theories have been advanced but no one has yet unlocked the secret of the constitutional impulse that sends birds on these great annual voyages.

Unlike ptarmigan, quail, and other members of the partridge family, which spend a lifetime in the neighborhood of one copse, enduring the extremes of climate, ducks choose their seasons. They avoid both the biting rigor of northern winters and the prostrating heat of southern summers. When the first mare's-tails of winter gather in the northern sky, they spread their wings for the southern migration. When sap rises in southern trees, they return to their nesting grounds. For them, years contain only two seasons—autumn and spring.

The morning following the arrival of a flight in Arkansas finds them rested. As they mill about, dive for acorns, and jump over one another in play, their talk is composed of sounds it is impossible to reconstruct with English syllables—sounds that can be found only in the lexicon of wildfowl. Often the conversation wells into a chorus with periodic crescendos. Natives term it the feeding call.

The display will continue until the flight is alarmed. Then, with a terrified quack, a hen vaults into the air! Instantly the water erupts ducks! A melee of flapping wings, craning necks, and swinging feet spouts forth in a bedlam of confusion. A turbulent surface marks their take-off. But the tumult is soon blotted out by the woods as they vanish through its tangle of branches.

Even if one watched this take-off intently, he would be unable to see what occurred, for the ducks *flew* out of the water. Each unfolded its wings, laid them flat upon the surface, and with one mighty downthrust of its pinions drove itself up and out of the water, carrying along a conical, diaphanous curtain of spray. Then, with a rapid wingbeat accompanied by a coordinated but ineffective pedaling of its webbed feet, it towered. When all seemed clear ahead, it leveled off in flight, feet nestling amid undertail coverts.

One never sees a duck *fly* out of the water. The wing motions are too rapid for human eyes to distinguish. Therefore one refers to a duck *jumping*, as though the action of the feet thrust it out of the water. This assumption is natural because the human eye cannot perceive the true movements!

Our eyes record an impression in one one-hundredth of a second, but retain it for one-tenth of a second. As each of the wing actions described takes place in less than the latter interval, the eye records the impression of a duck vaulting out of the water. Therefore one calls it jumping! Even such a careful observer as Audubon was misled. He noted that mallards "rise either from the ground or water with a single spring." He attributed a similar action to pintails, greenwings, and other river ducks. But a fast camera testifies that while these ducks spring from the ground, they *fly* out of water! If they were to beat the surface of ground as they do the surface of water, then underwing coverts and flight feathers as well would soon become torn and broken.

Flying out of water is characteristic of Anatinae, the subfamily of surface-feeding ducks that most commonly breed in and migrate over ponds, lakes, and rivers. Mallards, pintails, gadwalls, widgeons, shovellers, and teal belong to this subfamily. Sea and diving ducks of the subfamily Nyrocinae, such as canvasbacks, redheads, scaups, and scoters, rise from the water by a simultaneous flapping of wings and running on the surface. Scoters, which are less nimble, require a considerable distance to gather enough speed to permit being air-borne by wings alone. In their take-off they resemble heavily laden seaplanes taxiing along the surface, then flying long and low and bouncing back on the water several times before attaining enough speed to fly.

As fresh-water ducks usually inhabit reed- and grass-infested lakes, they seldom have enough unobstructed water for such a cumbersome getaway. To escape from danger requires a vertical getaway; it demands that they get out by flying directly up. Nature saw to it that they learned how.

Anatinae always face the wind when rising from water, but so dexterous are they in the manipulation of their wings they can throw themselves away from danger at the same time. In such cases, by rotating one extended wing one way and the other in the opposite direction, the initial downbeat spins the body as it is lifted out of the water so it faces the wind and is in position to receive its lifting force.

Or, if alarmed suddenly by an upwind danger, ducks may fly out of the water so rapidly that they lose their balance. Then, with heads far back, the first few wingbeats seemingly fly the birds backward and they occupy momentarily a position approaching inverted flight.

But not only do ducks approach inverted flight; at times they actually fly upside down! I have a slow-motion picture of a mallard hen flying toward me. Suddenly she became alarmed at the sound of the camera and changed her course quickly by doing what aviators in the last war called an Immelmann turn. She flew four wingbeats on her back and winged over, righting herself when headed safely away. In this volume are two series of photographs illustrating the start of similar maneuvers. But these motions were executed so rapidly they would not have been detected by one's eye.

Richard E. Bishop, America's foremost etcher of wildfowl whose sketches grace this volume, advises gunnermen never to criticize duck pictures with a "Ducks never do that." He cautions that it is better to say, "Ducks *seldom* do that." He has slow-motion pictures of birds flying backward, standing still in the air, and looping the loop, sometimes assuming unrealistic, even awkward, attitudes. I have seen his motion picture of a baldpate falling down a two-foot well of empty air into the water with a tremendous splash! The duck was coming in downwind and, in order to land, tried to turn into it sharply. It stalled on the turn and tumbled, going completely under the water. He has another picture of two mallards flying into decoys. The first hits an "air pocket," loses balance, rolls over on its back, flies that way for a couple of beats, rolls right side up again, and comes on. The second duck, flying about ten feet behind the leader, does not benefit from the latter's experience and goes through the identical performance.

But in these cases, also, an unaided human eye could not have detected what occurred; it would have appeared that the duck's flight merely faltered for an instant.

While level flight is the rule, when necessary a duck can perform any imaginable aerial maneuver, including any found in a stunt flier's bag of tricks. Furthermore, it will carry them out quicker, with more grace—and always come out of them a whole duck!

Such dexterity requires precise control over versatile and complex instruments—wings and tail.

FLYING OUT OF WATER . . . *Circles on the surface indicate that this drake has just pitched in, but an instant later he became alarmed. Photographs in this series were taken one-sixteenth of a second apart.*

He unfolds his wings .

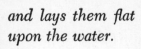

and lays them flat upon the water.

A mighty down-
thrust bends his
wings . . .

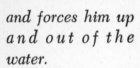

and forces him up
and out of the
water.

The first downbeat has raised him off the water about his own length, his wings now going back in recovery stroke.

6

7

Downstroke of the first wingbeat in the air.

8

The second recovery stroke.

9

Away! Primaries are bending under pressure. The time elapsing as this series was exposed was one-half second.

These drakes become alarmed! They face to the right, but, by twisting their right wings slightly during the initial downthrust, their bodies are turned as they rise.

The left one has momentarily lost balance. His tail is scooping air to right his body. Below: Out of the water. Less than one-quarter second later, they are in the air, having turned almost 90°.

Comedians of the marsh are the coots. Although members of the Rail family and not ducks, they are co-occupants with ducks of all inland marshes. Their pinwheel flight and nodding heads when swimming make them appear grotesque. Contrary to the notion prevalent among sportsmen, a coot's flesh is as tasty as that of a duck on the same feed. In order to popularize coots as game birds, Ducks Unlimited has re-christened them Whitebills. In sharp contrast to the manner of mallards, whitebills rise from the water like diving ducks by flapping of wings and running on the surface, sometimes using their wings, in the early part of their take-off, as though they were forelegs.

Canvasback running on the surface during take-off.

Diving ducks' legs are located farther back than river ducks' and, like this young canvasback's, protrude beyond their short tails in flight.

Flight feathers not fully grown prevent her take-off.

His craw bulging with rice as he drops into the flats for a siesta.

A whir of wings, a swish of air . . . blackjacks have come and gone.

Wily pintail

page 52

Every covert feather shows.

January pair

Chapter Four _____

THE SECRETS OF PINIONS

A mirrored lady

THE structure of a duck's wing is similar to that of a human arm but the proportions of hands and upper arms are reversed. A duck's "hand," the outer wing, to which are attached the ten long primary flight feathers, is much the longer section; its upper arm is short and almost concealed by the scapular feathers. Like most birds, a duck has almost as complete control over its wings as a man has over his arms, hands, and fingers.

Raise your arm so that it is parallel to the floor, then twist your hand so its plane is vertical to the floor—birds can do that with their wings! Separate your fingers; move them—birds can do that and more with their primary feathers! Shrug your shoulders—birds can do that! Raise your arms and clap your hands behind your head; now lower them and clap them behind your thighs—birds can do the same thing! Bring your hands up to your chest and bend your wrists, fingers pointing downward; your arm forms a letter Z—this is the position of a bird's wing in repose.

Have you ever floated lazily in the water, face down, and sculled forward slowly by bringing your arms downward and forward, hands twisted slightly so the motion pushed the water backward? That sculling action resembles the downbeat of bird wings in flight.

In the recovery, or upstroke, the bird's exquisite control over the intricate wing construction minimizes what might otherwise be a nullifying action, and this stroke, too, sometimes aids forward motion. The recovery stroke—accomplished in about one-half the time of the downbeat—is begun by lifting the wing wrists, which partly folds the wings. The primary feathers are separated to allow the passage of air between them and are rotated slightly to resemble slats of a Venetian blind opened obliquely to admit light. Then the hands are flipped upward quickly.

At the top of the stroke the primaries are closed; they again overlap like a closed Venetian blind and the outstretched wing, forming a slightly concave surface, is ready for the next downbeat.

The wingbeat cycle, even though composed of so many complicated movements, may take place with incredible rapidity. Hummingbirds' wings, for instance, beat at the fantastic speed of 100 to 200 times a second—so fast the wings have been "stopped" photographically only in laboratories with stroboscopic light. Quail beat their wings twenty times a second. At the bottom of the scale, pelicans and storks flap their large wings in their indolent flight but once or twice a second. Mallards in a hasty getaway speed their wingbeat up to ten or twelve times a second, but throttle down to eight when in cruising flight.

Among ducks, the smaller the bird the more rapid the wingbeat. Teal in normal flight flap their wings eleven times a second; pintails, nine times. But these are necessarily rough averages, because rapidity of wingbeat is related directly to speed. The faster any duck beats its wings, the faster it flies—just as a man moves his legs more rapidly when running than when walking.

These counts are of normal, sustained flight, equivalent in man to the cadence of a marching army.

The duck in my movies could not have done an Immelmann turn with her wings alone; the maneuver was accomplished largely with the aid of her tail. This dexterous instrument, like the tail of an airplane, helps determine the direction of flight; it is rudder and elevator combined. A duck has superlative control over it.

Depending upon species, a duck's tail is composed of sixteen to twenty short flight feathers. They project from its "Pope's Nose," which, forming the base of the tail, contains more than one thousand minute muscles to move the feathers.

A duck can move its tail in any direction—up, down, or sideways—or twist it. The tail feathers slide over each other more smoothly than the blades of any fan that ever came out of Japan; no geisha girl could open, twist, and play her fan as deftly as a duck maneuvers its tail feathers.

In straight, level flight, the feathers usually remain closed at the tip, forming a perfect, streamlined end to the bird's fuselage. The tail also maintains balance in flight; opening it shifts the center of air pressure backward. Preparatory to a change in elevation or direction, the tail feathers are opened like a fan till their arc sometimes covers 180 degrees. To aid in turning the body over, the plane of the tail feathers is rotated. The surface of an opened tail can be made flat, convex, or concave.

Just as the dainty geisha can manipulate her fan, a duck can open one side of its tail or the other and drop it or raise it. To stop suddenly or to slow flight, the tail is opened, cupped, and dropped simultaneously, making a very effective brake.

Thus the hen which performed the Immelmann for my camera spread her wings and fanned open and elevated her tail. This slowed her forward flight and dropped the after part of her body so that she zoomed up and over, making half a loop. Then she probably rotated it and made its plane slightly concave. This helped to turn her right side up. Later she folded it tightly, thus streamlining her body for a quick getaway.

If the mechanisms of ducks' wings and tails are remarkable, the construction and coloring of their feathers are even more so.

A flight feather's construction is an example of ingenious engineering; it combines strength, flexibility, smooth surface, and light weight. From opposite sides of a feather's central tapering shaft project hundreds of parallel, lath-shaped barbs. These barbs, which are clearly visible, form the vane. Each barb is in turn a miniature feather; it projects hundreds of tiny, invisible barbules which lap over those extending from the adjacent barbs. The barbules, in turn, have many microscopic, hook-like barbicels branching out from them. It is the function of these minute hooklets to seize hold of adjoining barbules like grapnels, thus giving the vane a strong, tight structure and smooth surface. Under the microscope, one sees this intricate, lattice-like arrangement forming a perfect herring-bone pattern.

The number of barbicels in a feather is prodigious. Professor J. A. Thomson states that 650 barbs were counted on the inner web of one of the primary feathers of a crane, and that each of these bore about 600 pairs of barbules, making 780,000 barbules for the inner web alone—much more than a million barbules for the whole feather! It follows, therefore, that this single feather had many million barbicels.

When separating the barbs of a flight feather, one is conscious of overcoming an amount of resistance that for such a delicate structure is considerable. The sensation is the same as though the barbs had been glued together. However, this resistance is the opposition offered by the barbicels' tight grasp on their neighboring barbules.

If one strokes the vane together again, these barbicels re-exert their grappling action. Even though the reunion is never good, it has been aptly termed nature's zipper action, for it is entirely mechanical.

When barbicels are not needed to impart strength nor to produce a smooth, streamlined surface, they are either reduced in number or absent entirely. There are no barbicels, for instance, in down feathers, whose function is to insulate the body. Down feathers are merely barbs tufted together with long, slender barbules. Incidentally, the "hairs" that one singes off a duck's breast before roasting are feathers, too—usually degenerate contour feathers.

Even if they were not damaged or broken by accident or predators, feathers would wear out with constant use. Hence nature provides for annual replacements. Soon after the hens begin the incubation of their eggs, the drakes leave them, seek seclusion, and moult. Shedding the brilliant, nuptial plumage they have worn since the previous winter, they take on a dull, inconspicuous eclipse plumage. Then they shed all flight feathers—primaries, outer secondaries, tail feathers—and some or all of the wing coverts. They are flightless for the month or so required for the replacements to grow.

The drake's eclipse plumage is almost indistinguishable from that of the hen. It is nature's camouflage designed to protect him against predators during his period of flightlessness.

In moulting, the feathers' quills, which are held at their bases in tube-like sheaths, loosen and the feathers drop out. Immediately replacement feathers form; soon they protrude from their sheaths as tiny spikes. Growth proceeds rapidly. After a few weeks, when they are fully developed, feathers receive no further blood or nourishment. As they contain no nerves, they are numb structures which may be torn or cut without causing pain.

Drakes moult again in the fall. This time, however, flight feathers are not shed. Only head and contour feathers are changed. Thus, by the time our gunning season starts, mallard drakes reappear in their familiar plumage. Other species are slower to change. In Arkansas, for instance, one seldom sees a widgeon in full nuptial plumage, or a shoveller in his green, cinnamon, and white dress and blue wings before December.

Ducks' eclipse plumage is a unique phenomenon. Dr. F. H. Kortright covers the subject this way: "The eclipse moult is peculiar to the duck, and is exhibited in no other kind of bird. Strangely enough, the eclipse is present only in the ducks of the northern hemisphere, not being found in those of the southern hemisphere, even in those countries where the climate is similar to that of the north, and even in ducks of the same species such as the cinnamon teals of North and South America."

Hens moult twice a year also. Their spring moult, when all but their flight feathers are replaced, is completed before nesting. And when the young ducklings are able to provide for themselves, usually five weeks or so after the drakes have commenced their moult, the hens go through a complete moult and a period of flightlessness.

Ducks' moulting process is another exception to nature's rule. Most birds retain their power of flight by shedding at any one time only one or two pairs of feathers from corresponding positions on each wing. One explanation offered for the ducks' method, which is also that of geese, is the desirability of perfect pinions for their long migration.

Richard Bishop suggests another explanation—that most birds must retain flying ability in order to get food, whereas ducks moult near ponds and marshes abounding with aquatic food-providing plants.

Frequent change of plumage, constant dusting, and preening make birds nature's best-dressed social order. Certainly they are the most richly caparisoned of all her creatures. No other members of the animal kingdom could wear such fresh and vivid colors as gracefully. The arrays displayed by such avian aristocrats as the stately wood duck and harlequin drake are truly exotic, yet, so carefully have the hues and tints been chosen and blended, they do not clash nor appear garish. Even a mallard drake's nuptial plumage is a glorious assembly of color. In my opinion, it does not receive the full appreciation its beauty warrants only because it is seen so frequently.

But of all the colors seen in feathers, few are caused by pigments. The colors of the most brilliant feathers result from the feathers' surface structure.

Blacks, browns, greys, reds, and some yellows are caused by pigments. But the red in hummingbirds and all iridescent colors—all blues, violets, some yellows, and glossy blacks—are caused by submicroscopic bars or prisms on the surface of barbules. They are structural colors. Greens are structural blues, topped with minute layers of yellow pigment.

Just as there is no color in the raindrops that produce a rainbow and as there is no pigmentation in soap capable of producing the iridescence of soap bubbles, there are no pigments in feathers to produce structural colors.

As rainbows result from the reflection, refraction, and dispersal of light into spectra, so the structural colors of birds result from *selective* reflections of light by feathers' submicroscopic bars.

In feathers, white is a structural color also. Clear ice is colorless. When fractured, however, ice turns white. This is because it can no longer transmit light; the fracture reflects light in all its hues. The result is a white color. Similarly, a white feather is one whose surface structure reflects all the hues of light. Therefore it appears white.

If one pulls out a mallard's secondary flight feathers composing the blue wing speculum or chevron—the brightly colored patch on its wing—and holds them up to light, no color will appear in the light transmitted through them. The chevron appears as a dull grey band. And if these feathers are subjected to pressure, the tiny prisms are broken and the blue color of the chevron disappears.

Sometimes the green head of a mallard drake seems to turn purple. Sometimes his chevron appears purple, sometimes a turquoise green. These changes result from variations in the incidence or quality of the light striking them or the angle from which they are viewed.

Feathers have always been both useful and ornamental to man. Those of eagles formed the war bonnets of our Indian chieftains. Their vanes guided the chieftains' arrows. For centuries the plumassier curled and dyed feathers for ladies of fashion. His plumes were awarded knights for prowess. Down feathers fill our pillows and line our sleeping bags and the flying suits of our bomber crews. And our grandparents used feather dusters to good effect.

It was with a feather's quill that Jefferson wrote the Declaration of Independence. It was with a quill that Hancock signed it in letters so large that "John Bull could read his name without putting on his specs."

Before writing his bold signature, I suppose Hancock sharpened his quill with a knife. Because small knives were used for this purpose, we still call them "pen knives." Even the word "pen" is derived from the word "penna"—Latin for feather. That the going with quills was not too smooth is indicated by the origin of our word "write." It is derived from the Anglo-Saxon "writan," meaning "scratch." From ancient times nigh unto the Twentieth Century, all the love letters of our ancestors, all poems, and all historical documents were "scratched" with quills. Audubon used the quills of trumpeter swans to draw the eyes and beaks of his small birds. And "Nature's greatest gift," wrote Lord Byron, "is my grey goose quill."

Bird feathers and bird flight have always fascinated man. He has envied birds the singular independence and speed imparted by wings—their ability to travel in three dimensions. He has wanted to experience the ecstasy of being wafted up to the heavens, and to soar from one end to the other of that mysterious abode of spiritual bliss. He has longed to mingle with clouds, celestial vapors, and the four winds, and to look down upon earth and all earth-bound life. Often he wished to exchange arms and hands, for a time at least, for wings and feathers. Countless men have speculated and innovated with flight in view. Leonardo da Vinci studied birds and designed methods of flight; Francis Bacon wrote about them. Thousands upon thousands have risked and surrendered their all in attempts to simulate birds. It is necessary to delve into mythology to find the first who paid this price—the end that befell Icarus with his wax-jointed wings.

Illustrative of this passionate yearning, it is significant that as an inspiration to goodness—as a reward for eschewing coarse and venal pleasures and obeying the Lord's Commandments—scores of generations have been promised the immortality symbolized by an angel—a pair of spiritual wings hereafter in the Kingdom of Heaven!

Biologists teach that, together with all animals, man and bird had common ancestry in reptiles. In birds, reptilian forelegs evolved into wings, scales into feathers. In man, the reptilian forelegs evolved into arms, scales into skin, which, incidentally, is composed of minute scales. Gordon Aymar states: "It has been estimated that under the skin of a goose are twelve thousand muscles whose only function is to control the action of feathers." As ducks belong to the same family, they must possess a similar number.

The photographs on the opposite page are after the manner of C. W. Beebe's illustrations in The Bird.

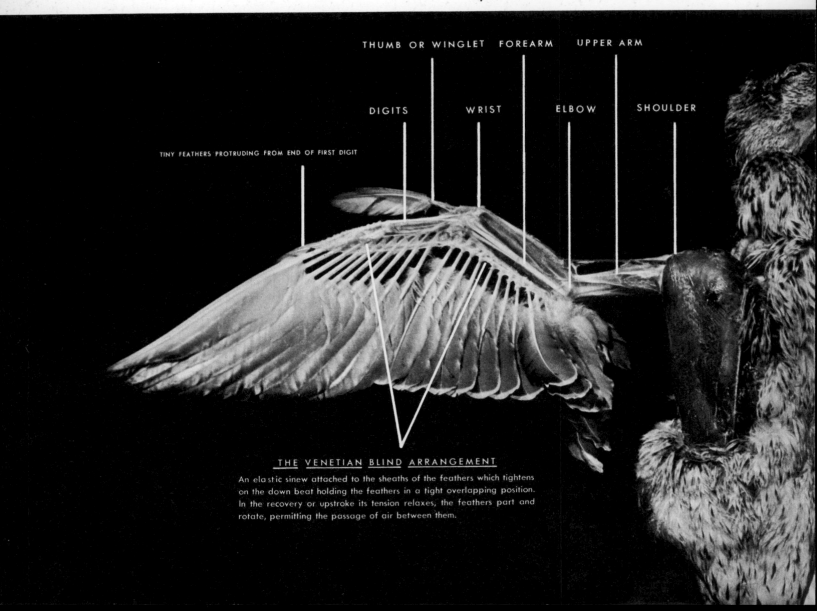

THUMB OR WINGLET   FOREARM   UPPER ARM

DIGITS   WRIST   ELBOW   SHOULDER

TINY FEATHERS PROTRUDING FROM END OF FIRST DIGIT

THE VENETIAN BLIND ARRANGEMENT

An elastic sinew attached to the sheaths of the feathers which tightens on the down beat holding the feathers in a tight overlapping position. In the recovery or upstroke its tension relaxes, the feathers part and rotate, permitting the passage of air between them.

Wing of mallard drake. The thumb, or winglet, from which three feathers project, has been raised.

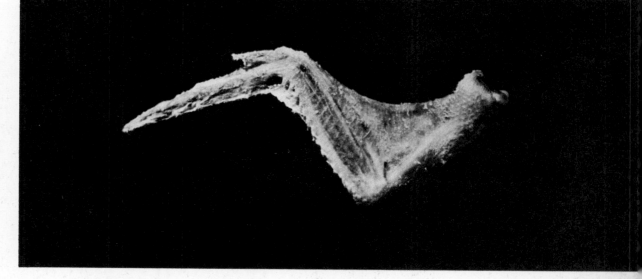

Same wing, with feathers removed, thumb raised—second and third digits, to which the primaries were attached, point downward.

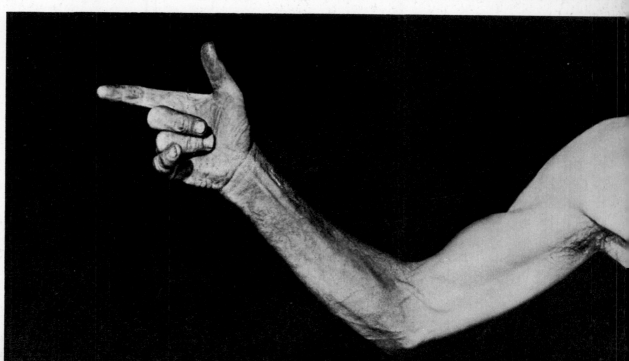

Man's arm in corresponding position.

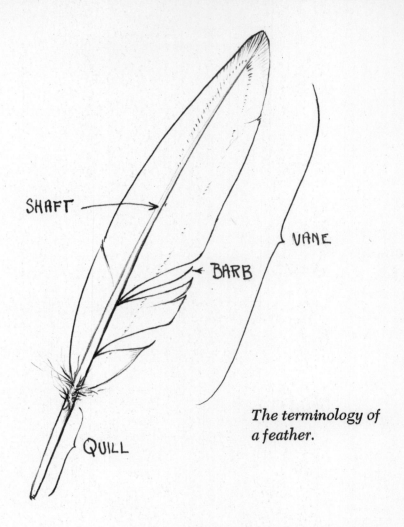

*The terminology of
a feather.*

At the top of the opposite page is a section of a mallard's primary, enlarged about sixty times. The herring-bone pattern formed by the interweaving barbules is evident. Barbules angling off from the right sides of the barbs, while straighter than those of the left, appear to twist, so that the barbicels attached to the spiral-like barbules emerging from the left sides of the barbs may grapple them effectively.

The distance marked "A" on the micron scale of the center photograph is 17/10,000ths of an inch. Hence, the width of the vane of this barb is about 2/100th of an inch. Only one side of the vane carries barbicels, which fasten onto the barbules of the adjoining barb.

The photomicrographs on the opposite page were made in cooperation with N. R. Piesbergen of Monsanto Chemical Company's Biological Research Laboratories.

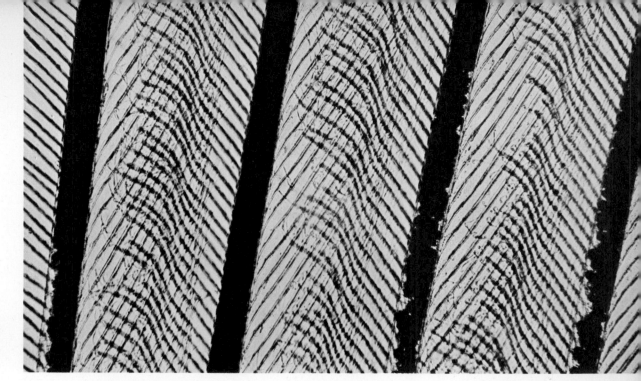

Barbs and barbules form a herring-bone pattern.

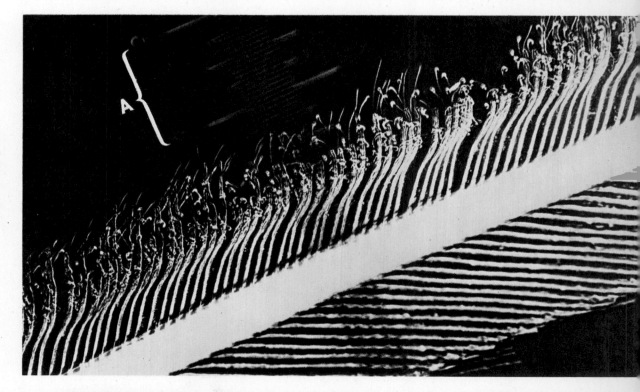

This is a barb — a minute feather in itself. The width of this barb's vane is about 1/50th of an inch.

Hook-like barbicels at the end of a barbule, magnified about 500 times.

St. Louis Zoo mallard drake in eclipse plumage.

The mallard hen in the lower illustration, also an inhabitant of the St. Louis Zoo, where they are fed but otherwise allowed freedom in full wing, has completed her post-nesting moult; new flight feathers are seen emerging from their shafts. New, short, sabre-like coverts are emerging between the primaries.

At the top of opposite page is the wing of an eight-week-old drake. His juvenile flight feathers, with which he would have learned to fly, are emerging from their shafts. The filoplumes, which he has worn since he shed down in their favor, are still attached to the ends of two primaries, several coverts, and one thumb feather. He would have worn these flight feathers until the following spring.

This hen is growing new flight feathers.

Eight - week - old mallard drake's wing.

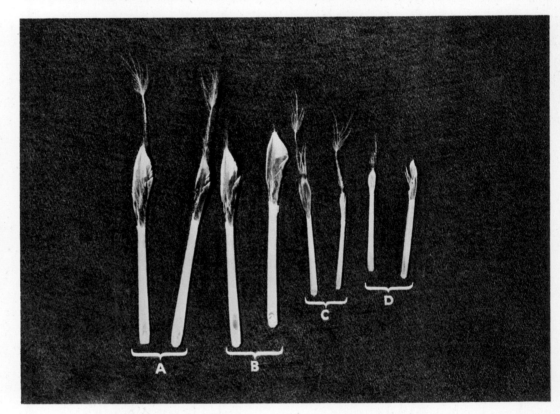

Feathers unroll as they grow out of shafts. A & B are primaries — C & D are greater wing coverts. Filoplumes still attached to the tips of A & C.

Mallard tail feathers, as described in Addendum, page 247. A, from adult hen; B, juvenile drake.

Upper-body feathers

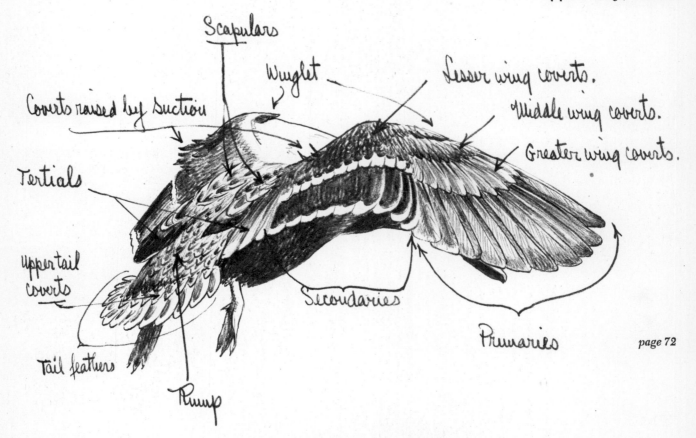

Scapulars

Winglet

Lesser wing coverts.

Middle wing coverts.

Greater wing coverts.

Coverts raised by suction

Tertials

Upper tail coverts

Secondaries

Primaries

Tail feathers

Rump

Under-body feathers

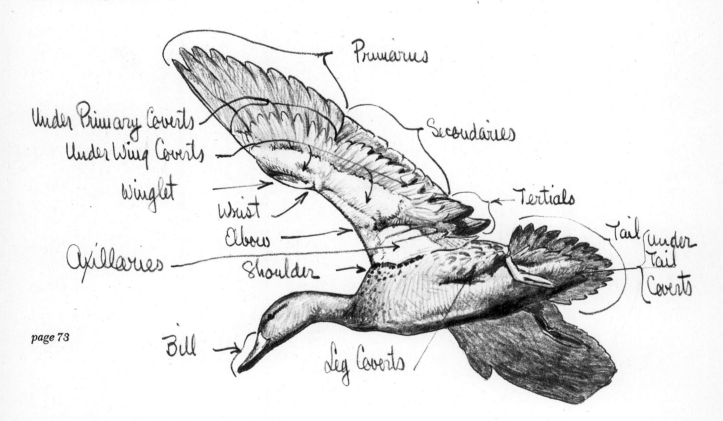

Primaries

Under Primary Coverts
Under Wing Coverts
Winglet

Secondaries

Tertials

Wrist
Elbow

Axillaries

Shoulder

Tail
Under Tail Coverts

Bill

Leg Coverts

Getting away

An anserine armada deploys over the blind.

The smallest of the swiftest—female green-winged teal. Even a bluewing is larger than this smallest of all North American ducks. According to Kortright, the average weight of greenwing hens is but twelve ounces, yet greenwings are among the fastest fliers and the hardiest of the entire duck family.

One distinguishing feature of a wood duck in the air is the square-shaped tail. His flight is fast; he has a high ratio of wing area to body weight and his relatively large tail makes for quick, sharp turns so necessary for flying among trees. The "woodie" is a true North American duck; he is not found in any other part of the world.

Time to shove safeties off!

As these drakes clear the sweet gum, each puts his tail to different use. The lowest has opened his tail as he changes elevation. The center one's tail is partly folded, and his wings are advanced, while the uppermost, apparently content with his elevation and direction, has his tail closed and wings in cruising flight position.

In the air, sprigs are characterized by long bodies, pointed tails and slender, pointed wings. To Bishop, the drakes seem to have on full-dress suits, "they look so immaculate with their dark heads, white breasts, and dark tails." Such formally attired gentlemen predominate in this photograph; of 35 ducks in the flight, only 8 are hens.

The shoveller is an early fall visitor to Arkansas and one of the last to depart in the spring. Instead of diving or tipping up for its food, the shoveller prefers very shallow water wherein it can comb the bottom for food. This it washes in its huge bill by shaking its head from side to side, the row of large bristles serving as a sieve.

Indians called shovellers Soo'-choo-koo, after the low-pitched call of this unusually quiet species. It is a more euphonious name than our colloquial ones, such as spoonbill, Hollywood mallard, cowfrog, laughing mallard, shovelnose, broadbill and souplips. They are omnivorous ducks, but when feeding on Arkansas rice they are as tasty as any other. A shoveller drake's eclipse plumage not only makes him indistinguishable from a hen, but his black bill also takes on her greenish-orange color.

page 83

The pintail's long and graceful neck must be advantageous when tipping up for food.

Pintails are always among the first fall arrivals in Arkansas; some remain for the winter. Late January sees their number augmented by those from the Gulf Coast pressing northward as winter retreats. Pintails are usually the first ducks to return to their nesting grounds.

One duck never flies directly behind another. It flies below, above, or aside. Thus they not only avoid each other's air stream, but they have a clear view ahead.

page 86

Venetian blinds in action! The sun is peeping through his primaries as they open during a recovery stroke, casting zebra-like shadows on his breast and serrated ones on his under wing.

Changing direction

Chapter Five

INSTRUMENTS OF FLIGHT

Midway on downbeat and recovery

Technics of Wings _____

EVER since human history emerged, nature has been man's fount of inspiration. Mute, uttering not one syllable comprehensible as a word to the human ear, she was, nevertheless, his primeval teacher; she provides his lessons today. Throughout all time she has offered stimulating examples for him to emulate; her processes ever gave broad hints for him to follow.

Consequently, as time unfolded and, one after another, man perceived her works, he conceived methods of imitation. Although in a few cases the precocious pupil has apparently excelled his teacher, it was not until he turned scientist that he understood and mastered many of her processes. But even as a scientist, man still is woefully primitive; the secret of chlorophyll, upon which all life on his own planet depends, has not yet been unlocked. It was but yesterday that he perceived, to Japan's great regret, why our sun burns without burning out; that as elements may be transformed, they are not elementary, and that atoms, being divisible, were indeed misnamed. And these new perceptions, like all preceding ones, originated by observing nature—the slow disintegration of uranium. Indeed, all of man's progress may be traced to his observation of nature's examples and nature's methods, then emulating them with adaptations of her own stores.

It seems evident, for instance, that in the dim past some imaginative savage must have gazed upon a leaf drifting on a pool of water or a limb floating downstream and, perceiving that anything lighter than water would float, conceived the idea that a hollowed-out tree trunk would provide water-borne transportation. Similarly, when lightning set a forest afire, another must have become aware of the comfort of fire's warmth and how much more tasty was a deer which, having been trapped in its path, was roasted in its flame. This quick-witted one perceived that sparks made fire, that friction made sparks, then conceived a method of kindling fire himself.

If our primal forests had not teemed with hairy animals, man would not have perceived that their skins gave warmth and protection, and then conceived the idea of stripping fur off animals to wear himself. It is possible that a rolling stone provided the conception of the wheel; we know that lightning acquainted man with the phenomenon of electricity.

The list of his achievements, accumulated over millenniums, is now a formidable one, but the record reveals that man has never been original. He has always been engaged in fathoming the how and why of nature's works and processes and in imitating them. Furthermore, through all time his consciousness has been impregnated with the inviolability of the natural phenomena surrounding him. A Siamese king of the last century provides an illustrative case. This monarch declared his Dutch Minister mad because the latter insisted that in Holland water became so hard in winter people walked upon it. The unfortunate minister was banished! Because he had never seen ice, His Majesty was incapable of conceiving water as anything other than a tepid liquid. Does it not seem unlikely that refrigeration, which duplicates a natural transformation, could have been conceived in Siam, where this natural transformation was never observed?

Ever since he developed a consciousness, man has been aware of the inviolability of the earth's gravity; every footstep, every falling leaf reminded him of it, as the apple which is supposed to have dropped upon Isaac Newton's head caused him to ponder why the apple fell. In view of this mental attitude, is it not unlikely that man would have had sufficient imagination to conceive of flight without the natural example of birds? Without the proof constantly offered by birds that gravity could be overcome, would he have had the audacity to conceive of the possibility of something heavier than the air sustaining itself in the air?

But, in any case, birds were an ever-present reminder to man that gravity could be defied; that he, too, might fly if he gained their secrets. This prospect fascinated him. In consequence, he has been pondering bird flight and studying the form and structure of bird wings for countless centuries. Long before Aristotle wrote about flight, ancients believed that on the summits of mountains they approached the oracle of heaven, home of birds and the supernatural. Mythologies deal with flight; gods and mythological figures were often endowed with powers of flight. But so slowly did man progress that when Lord Kelvin was asked how birds soared, he replied, "That which puzzled Solomon puzzles me."

Even as recently as 1891 Otto Lilienthal, the father of gliding experiments, wrote wistfully of the "beauty and perfection of birds' movements, the efficiency and safety of their flying apparatus," and expressed the hope that the time was not far distant "when our knowledge and understanding of the method of flight will enable us to break the spell which has so far made it impossible to free our foot from Mother Earth even for one voluntary flight."

Somewhat earlier, Lilienthal had built wings for himself from "sticks of . palisander wood, pointed and rounded, which served as quills for two wings three metres long each. The feathers of these quills were represented by a series of large goose feathers which were sewn on tape. . . . The sewing on of these quills was very troublesome and fatiguing for the fingers, and many a drop of blood upon the white feathers testified to the damage done to our fingertips." These wings, strapped around his waist, were moved by a "stirrup arrangement." But as he "did not heed the lesson taught by our storks," the machine came to an inglorious end. This event occurred within the memory of men now living. Countless generations had made the effort but they failed to solve the enigma.

However, Lilienthal and others persevered. Consequently, when the internal combustion engine appeared, these pioneers had laid the foundation for the airplane. And during recent years, as knowledge of aerodynamics expanded, airplane designs approximated more and more the form of a bird. Box-kite-like triplanes and biplanes gave way to monoplanes, the square-shaped fuselage to a rounded, birdlike one. Modern streamlining now simulates a bird's body. Retractable landing gears imitate the retraction of a bird's feet when in flight. Even such devices as wing slots and wing flaps have their counterparts in birds.

How does this supreme achievement of nature, whose form our aerodynamicists emulate and whose mechanisms they borrow, sustain itself in the air?

When Glenn Martin told me that "a bird supports its weight and also obtains its propelling force by *causing air to flow over and under its wings*," I was puzzled. I had observed bird flight carefully for many years; I had read about it; I had studied slow-motion pictures of it. Yet I believed that a bird sculled its way through the air by forcing its *wings through* the air downward and forward, then upward and backward, pressure and suction holding it aloft and moving it ahead.

But my notion was a naive oversimplification.

Perhaps it is well to precede the following dissertation on Glenn Martin's concise statement with a confession that it embraces a considerable amount of intellectual freebootery. I have picked Glenn Martin's mind and the minds of his engineers as well. I have helped myself liberally to Dick Bishop's stores of knowledge and benefited wherever possible by searching rapaciously other sources of information in libraries.

But the yield from libraries was very disappointing. Ornithologists have written profusely about birds' life histories and anatomies, without leaving any considerable evidence that they concerned themselves with how these anatomies functioned in the air. And aerodynamic engineers, it seems, are like Spartans—"bold men of short sentences." I found no literature indicating that any one of them has applied to bird flight up-to-date technical knowledge, in spite of the fact that in the light of this knowledge a great deal of that which has been written contains misleading conclusions. This book is not intended to fill the void; its scope is much too limited. The field is calling for an intensive inquiry by a modern Lilienthal.

Because technical terms might offer obstacles to some readers, I have been tempted to hasten over a description of bird flight with just enough generalities to satisfy normal curiosities—as a Chinese proverb characterizes "essays," to "chatter with a pen" about it. But it seems desirable to risk a few pages that might deter some readers in order to offer to the studious and inquiring mind a few fundamentals necessary to an understanding of it.

To do so requires a brief venture into the realm of aerodynamics. And, as we should understand its language, it seems desirable to pause for a few definitions. I have attempted to by-pass technical words, but without success. If we are to analyze a bird as a machine, we must employ mechanical terms.

Aerodynamics—treats of the laws of *air in motion* and the mechanical effects produced.

Airfoil—an object with flat or curved surfaces which produces reactions, such as lift or drag, when moved through the air; wings of planes and birds are airfoils, as are airplane rudders and ailerons. Even a single feather may act as an airfoil.

Angle of Attack—the pitch at which an airfoil meets the air stream. If the major axis is parallel to the air stream the "angle of attack" is zero. The greater the inclination with respect to the air stream the higher the "angle of attack."

Stall—a condition where the "angle of attack" is so great that the air stream no longer flows over the upper surface of an airfoil. It has broken away; its lifting power no longer sustains the foil's weight.

Camber—an upwardly convex shape.

Parallelogram of Forces—a mechanical law that the resultant of two forces represented in magnitude and direction by two adjacent sides of a parallelogram is represented by the magnitude and direction of the diagonal of the parallelogram.

Let us commence by referring to Mr. C. T. Ludington's *Smoke Streams*. He has generously permitted me to quote, interpolate, and paraphrase several of its passages and reproduce some of its diagrams and illustrations. Although he wrote for students of aviation, the book's text and its illustrations are helpful to an understanding of bird flight. Engineers may find some of the passages, as I have used them, faulty. If so, it is the result of omitting some of Mr. Ludington's amplifying and qualifying statements. Also, I have avoided his distinctions between types of airplane apparatus. For our broad purpose, for instance, we are not concerned with the differentiation between a so-called simple wing flap and a split wing flap. Therefore this attempt to achieve brevity as well as simplicity sacrifices some of the original's accuracy.

To visualize air flow behavior, Mr. Ludington photographed models in the Griswold smoke stream tunnel. In effect it is a wind tunnel, small streams of white smoke being introduced into its air stream, enabling one to see its disturbance and flow around models, much as one can see the waves and wake of a ship passing through water. The results duplicated conditions that would be created if the airfoil models had been pulled through still air.

Mr. Ludington's opening chapter describes the forces of an air stream. The following paraphrases some of its pertinent paragraphs:

The force acting upon a body placed in a moving stream of air has two components: a *vertical* force acting at *right angles to the air stream* and a *horizontal* force acting *downstream* in the direction of the air stream, caused by the resistance of the body to the moving air. The *vertical force* is called '*lift*' and the *horizontal* force '*drag*.'

Figure 1 carries a parallelogram of forces of these two components, lift and drag, acting on an airfoil and indicating the direction of the resultant force.

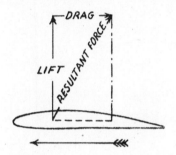

Fig. 1. *Forces acting on wing section.*
All diagrams in this chapter are illustrative and not quantitative.

The amount of lift on a given body placed in a moving stream of air depends upon three factors: the shape of the body as presented to the air flow, the speed of the air, and the density of the air.

To understand this, we must first understand the principle of fluid motion, i.e., *the total energy of a particle in motion is constant at all points on its path in a steady flow.* This means that the *total energy of air* in motion at any point equals the *static* pressure *plus the dynamic pressure*. Let us think of static pressure as forces exerted on the top and bottom surfaces of an airfoil, and dynamic pressure as the forces exerted in the direction of the flow.

Since the principle of fluid motion states that *the total of the two pressures must remain constant,* it follows that *if one of them is increased the other will decrease.* Therefore, increasing air flow speed over an airfoil, which increases the dynamic pressure, will lower the static pressure. (Figure 2)

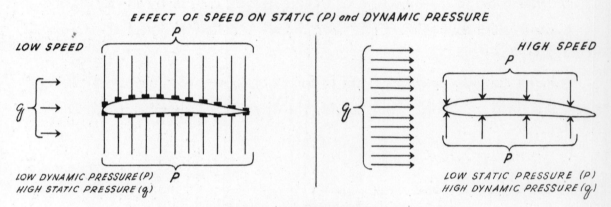

Fig. 2. *Static and dynamic pressure.*

Figure 3 illustrates this principle in a smoke tunnel. Two airfoil sections were connected to a common support in a manner allowing movement of the sections according to the effects of static and dynamic pressures. The curved surfaces of the airfoils faced each other and the flat surfaces faced outward. The air current was started slowly and gradually increased. With low velocity, the airfoils stayed some distance apart; as the velocity was increased, they moved closer together.

The explanation of this phenomenon is this: The air which flows between the curved surfaces moves faster than the air in the rest of the stream because it is compressed into a smaller space. This means that the *static pressure on the inside surfaces is decreased because the dynamic pressure has been increased;* therefore the static pressure on the outside surfaces is greater than that on the inside surfaces and the two airfoils are brought together and held there.

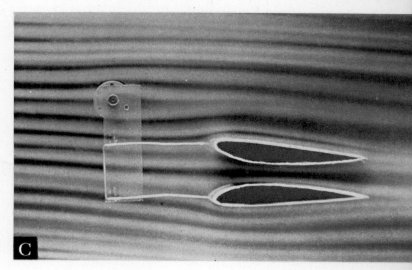

Fig. 3. *Effect of air speed on static and dynamic pressures.*

> A. *Air velocity = 15 mph. Airfoils stay far apart.*
>
> B. *Air velocity = 30 mph. Airfoils move closer.*
>
> C. *Air velocity = 45 mph. Airfoils move still closer.*

These and all ensuing Smoke Streams *photographs reproduced from the book by C. T. Ludington.*

Then, as the velocity of the air is increased, the static pressure on the inside surfaces is still further decreased and the airfoils move still closer together. The forces which move the airfoils together are the same forces we call lift.

Top-surface lift is illustrated in a simple experiment anyone can perform. Take a piece of paper and let it hang over the top edge of a book. Hold the book in front of your face at an angle to your mouth and blow on it. The hanging paper will rise up into the air. (Figure 4)

If the reader has not understood the foregoing paraphrase I suggest rereading and, if necessary, rereading it again. It is essential to understand the principles expounded if one desires to understand the principles of flight. They are its very essence.

As noted in the parallelogram of forces in Figure 1, the forces occurring on an airfoil passing through air results in two components. The force in the direction of the resultant air stream is called *drag*, the vertical component is

Fig. 4. *Simple illustration of top-surface lift.*

called *lift*. In the case of an airplane, drag is counter-balanced by the propeller, but birds must counter it by wing movement. In cruising flight, they accomplish this result by inclining the plane of their wings relative to their body during downstrokes so that when air passes over them the resultant force is in an upward and forward direction. (Figure 5)

Fig. 5. *Downbeat.*

Figure 6 visualizes, in a series of smoke-stream photographs, the action of an air stream on an airfoil whose cross-section approximates that of a bird's wing. If speed is constant, up to a certain point lift increases as the angle of attack becomes more oblique. Drag, the resistance of the air to the forward motion of the airfoil, increases also. These results may be attained not only by raising a wing's angle of attack, but by increasing its camber, i.e., by making the parabolic curvature of its surfaces more pronounced. Many photographs in this book illustrate that high degrees of drag are utilized by birds when stopping and turning.

Perhaps through these illustrations of the functioning of the principle of fluid motion we may now understand Glenn Martin's statement that a bird flies "by causing air to flow over and under its wings." We have seen that this results in a combination of forces—the upper surface providing top-surface lift, which is utilized by the bird for forward motion, as well as forces that sustain the bird in the air while pressure on the under side of the wing complements both.

There is an over-all similarity between the functioning of a bird's wings and those of an airplane—or, more properly, a glider—but it is limited to the form of flight known as soaring. In soaring, the air motion requisite to sustain an air-foil is provided by rising currents of air. In all other types of flight, the functions of bird wings include not only those of airplanes but others as well. Therefore their mechanisms differ from those of airplane wings; they are far more complex.

The wing of an airplane is fixed with respect to the fuselage; it is immobile except when bending under the stress of steep banks and turns. If one disregards the action of ailerons and wing flaps, an airplane wing's angle of incidence, as related to the fuselage, is constant; its camber is unalterable. In contrast, bird wings are flexible; they can be moved up, down, forward, and backward at the shoulder and they can be rotated at the shoulder to vary the angle of attack of the whole wing. Furthermore, as they are jointed at the elbow and again at the wrist, the angle of attack of each of the wing sections may be changed independently of the others.

These different sections usually perform different functions at the same time. In cruising flight, for instance, the section extending to the wrist—that portion containing the tertials and secondary feathers—provides most of the forces that sustain a bird in the air, whereas the propelling forces increase progressively outward, the hand bearing the primary feathers providing the greatest part. In addition a bird can change the camber—or parabolic curvature—of its wings by bending its elbows. Drag increases with the degree of this curvature. Small camber is used in cruising flight when the angle of attack is such that the resultant force not only sustains the bird but propels it forward. Conversely, in pitching and hovering, when forward movement is not wanted, wing camber is increased.

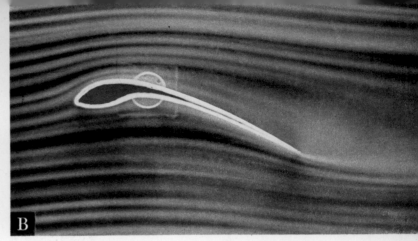

Angle of attack = 0°.   Fig. 6.   *Angle of attack increased.*

Moreover, at times a bird uses one wing in a different manner from the other. Although tail and feet are auxiliary controls for changing the direction of flight, wings are the most effective instruments employed. For instance, if a bird desires to turn to the right, its right wing makes a longer sweep and beats faster, while the angle of attack of the left wing is increased and the bird is banked into a right turn. If it desires to climb, the wings move forward at the shoulder and their angle of attack is increased.

Birds use their wings in different manners in different types of flight—horizontal, descending, gliding, soaring, hovering, taking off, and climbing. Furthermore, each of the various types of birds, such as waterfowl, soarers, and those of the forest floor, has differently shaped and proportioned wings and moves them in a distinctive manner. For instance, the wingbeat of a soaring bird, such as a gull, in normal cruising flight covers an arc scarcely half that of a wild duck. The wingbeats of quail, grouse, pheasants, and wild turkeys are interrupted by short bursts of soaring. As the subject encompasses so many variables, no attempt will be made to cover them. This brief description, while embodying principles applicable to all birds in flapping flight, is relevant particularly to the field of this work—the flight of ducks.

In straight, horizontal flight, the duck's wingbeat arc is relatively small and the stroke, as related to the ground, is oblique. As related to its body, the stroke is downward and forward. On the downbeat the wing's leading edge is lower than its trailing edge; the angle of attack is low, the resultant force providing enough lift to sustain the bird in the air and propel it forward. (Figure 7). Re-

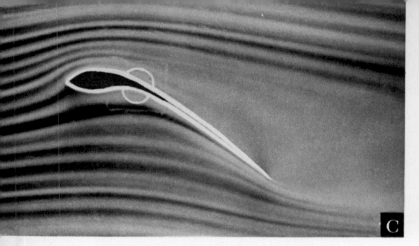
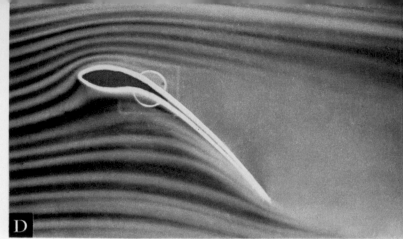

C   D

sistance offered by the streamlined shape of its body is small. Consequently, the forces required to maintain a constant forward speed are not great and most of the wing action results in forces that overcome gravity. If the duck desires to accelerate its pace, it rotates its wings at its shoulders, lowering the leading edge further, speeds up the wingbeat, and increases its arc. For an explanation of the mechanical rudiments involved in forward flight, read Glenn Martin's notes on page 239.

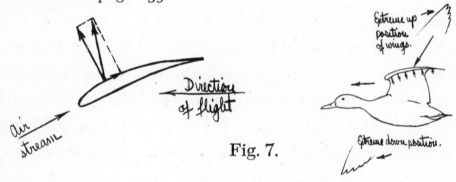

Fig. 7.

When dropping down or hovering, the wingbeat arc is almost parallel to the ground. The wingbeat is usually slowed and the angle of attack increased so the resultant force is mostly vertical. If there is a wind, the bird usually utilizes it by pitching into it, as indicated in Figure 8.

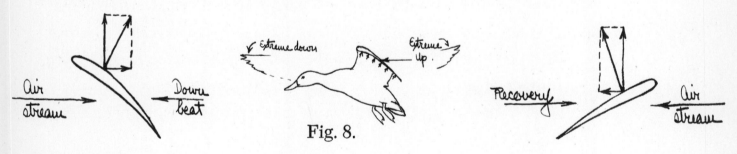

Fig. 8.

Fig. 9.

When taking off from water, a river duck's initial downbeat is nearly verti-cal; the plane of the wing being laid on the surface of the water itself is parallel to it. The resultant forces lift the bird. If there is a wind the take-off is usually made into it, but if the bird is alarmed and the take-off has been sudden, and if the wind does not blow from the direction of a point of danger, it turns into it as soon as possible. (Figure 9)

Once off the water, if the duck continues climbing its wingbeat resembles that used in dropping down or hovering. With a great angle of attack, the wings beat rapidly; the stroke is sweeping and vigorous, taxing the very power-ful pectoral muscles to the utmost. If the duck rises vertically, the wingbeat and air forces resemble those pictured in Figure 8. If both altitude and for-ward movement are desired, the wingbeat approximates some compromise between those pictured in Figures 7 and 8.

Geese and diving ducks are handicapped by having a low ratio of wing area to body weight. When they take off from water or land they run into the wind, using both wings and feet until the air stream is of sufficient force to provide enough lift for them to rise. If there is a good wind this air stream is created quickly, but if there is a calm the run is often a prolonged one. My slow-motion

pictures indicate that, in the absence of wind, canvasbacks take twenty or more steps on the water and about a dozen wingbeats before they are off. One of a young ruddy duck shows him taking thirty-nine hurried steps, yet he was far from clear when the camera ran down. Mr. Ludington cited another instance of the importance of wind in these take-offs: "I am reminded of an incident that interested a group of us very much when we were air-minded kids in the Adirondack-Florida School about 1910 or '11. Not far from the school in the Adirondacks there was a tiny pond which was quite shallow and surrounded by some high trees. For this reason we could skate on it much earlier in the season than on other larger ones. One day we walked down in the afternoon to see whether there were signs of ice. There were none and we were disappointed until we scared up a loon which tried to take off. Beginning its run at one end of the pond, it was unable to climb steeply enough and did not attempt a turn when it saw it could not clear the trees at the end. It flopped down into marshy ground some twenty feet shy of the trees. Other boys saw the loon still on the pond a day or so later. Then, one night we had a very strong wind; and as soon as we got out of school the next day, a number of us ran out to the pond and discovered that the loon had been able to take off."

That the large, webbed feet of geese and diving ducks play an important part in the take-off is indicated by one of Dick Bishop's moving pictures in which a flock of geese standing on a frozen pond attempts to take off in calm air. They have a most difficult time as their feet skid awkwardly on the ice, and a very considerable run, in which the wings are obviously the only accelerating force, is

required before any of them are able to rise. One goose, having a slightly damaged wing, surrenders to the situation in amusing dismay after several prolonged and fruitless attempts.

High-Lift Features

Birds also incorporate features known in airplanes as "high-lift devices." Ludington defines a high-lift device as one that "either increases the amount of lift on an airfoil at a given angle or maintains its lift properties up to a higher angle of attack." Some of them, he points out, are useful only to decrease landing speeds; others help in taking off.

In airplanes, wing slots, which are either fixed or movable devices attached to the wing's leading edge, allow some control over the air stream which flows over the wing's upper surface. Wing flaps increase the effective camber of the wing and its angle of attack; when depressed to great angles they also greatly increase drag and act as airbrakes.

"The leading edge slot," Ludington points out, "is very successful in keeping a smooth flow of air over the top surface of the airfoil at higher angles than the plain airfoil could reach. Figure 10 shows a view of the air flow through a leading edge slot at a high angle of attack. Note how smoothly the smoke streams flow through the slot and cling to the top surface of the airfoil. In practical use the leading edge slot is closed at high speed and low angles of attack. It opens automatically as the angle of attack passes a certain point and the speed is reduced."

In ducks, the thumb, or winglet, performs in a small way the function of a leading edge slot. Paralleling Ludington's description of the functioning of an airplane's leading edge wing slots, a duck's winglets lie closely against the leading edges of its wings in cruising flight when the wings have a low angle of attack. In fact, they form a part of this neatly rounded edge. But they are usually raised when turning, pitching, and landing, and they are often raised when climbing. To describe this action of a winglet, one might almost use Ludington's words describing the action of an airplane's wing slot—"It opens automatically as the angle of attack passes a certain point."

Fig. 10. *Passing through a wingslot, smoke stream clings to the top surface.*

The function of a wing flap is performed in part by the duck's tail, although the wings participate also. When a duck is pitching in, for instance, the camber of the wing itself is increased by pulling in the wrists and bending the elbow, and the tail is dropped and cupped. Figure 11 of an airfoil with wing slots and flap illustrates a wing's angle of attack and the functioning of winglets and tail when a duck is pitching.

Some of the photographs in this book show ruffled wing coverts. Their condition may be traced to a condition of stall—the angle of attack having been increased beyond the point where lift results (D, Figure 6). In this case the air flow no longer follows the contour of the wing's upper surface, and a condition

Fig. 11. *Functioning of winglet and tail when pitching.*

known as "flow separation" has taken place. When this occurs, a partial vacuum on the upper wing surface results and the coverts are pushed out of place by a reversed air flow rushing over the area. Figure 12, drawn by one of Glenn Martin's engineers, illustrates how such a reversed flow raises feathers.

This is the condition indicated in D, Figure 6. It occurs frequently when ducks are dropping down or pitching. Then the air stream presses against the wings' under surfaces, and the wings' upper surfaces are not producing lift but drag.

The Recovery Stroke

So FAR we have concerned ourselves particularly with the downbeat of the wing, which in forward flight provides most or all of the propelling force, but the recovery stroke contributes to flight also. In the recovery stroke, which is accomplished in about half the period of the downbeat, the wings are

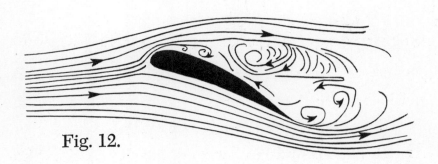

Fig. 12.

bent at the wrists and rotated at the shoulders so that the angle of their plane at the top of the upbeat, as related to the ground, is reversed.

At the beginning of the stroke the primaries are opened and rotated, allowing air to pass between them freely, and each vane acts as a miniature airfoil—the Venetian blind arrangement. The secondaries likewise open slightly, permitting some passage of air. Midway in the recovery stroke the primaries begin closing; they overlap each other again during the quick backward flip which completes the stroke and places the wings in position for the next downbeat. All of these manipulations are amplified greatly during pitching, hovering, and climbing.

Judging by the relative size of the two pectoral muscles controlling the wing-beat, the downbeat employs very much more energy than the upbeat. The large depressor muscle, which pulls the wing down, is many times the size of the elevator muscle, which raises it. Incidentally, the latter muscle in an ingenious manner acts on a tendon which passes through an eyelet in the shoulder, then doubles back and attaches itself to the top of the wing's upper arm. It acts as a pulley. When the elevator muscle contracts it pulls one end of the tendon down; the other end pulls the wing up.

In addition to the much larger size of the depressor muscle, F. W. Headley thinks it is stronger, weight for weight, because it "is a redder, rougher, more granulated muscle and its color and texture are indicative of superior quality."

I have been unable to ascertain the extent of the contribution, if any, the recovery stroke makes in a duck's normal cruising flight. It seems certain that the inner wing, which receives the air stream resulting from the bird's forward motion, creates sufficient lift to sustain it. And Gordon Aymar quotes authorities such as E. H. Hankin and Professor Marey as expressing "little room for doubt that the backward flip" aids forward flight.

However, in pitching, hovering, or climbing vertically, it is evident that the recovery stroke, especially the quick backward flip, contributes substantially to lift. It is performed with great vigor. In these types of flight, there is little or no forward motion of the duck itself through the air to nullify the creation of lifting forces by the backward speed of the outer wing. Even the angle of attack of the opened primaries indicates that each one, acting as a miniature airfoil, is making its own tiny contribution.

If consideration is given to the handicaps under which their authors worked, my reference to some older interpretations of bird flight have not been generous. Wing motion takes place with such rapidity that the human eye is incapable of perceiving the many minute and complicated motions involved. Those authors did not have up-to-date engineering knowledge and photographic apparatus at their disposal. It is only with modern cameras and film that the functioning of wing feathers and wing sections at various infinitesimal instants can be conveyed to the human mind in a manner permitting apprehension of the meanings.

Ultra-slow-motion pictures prolong these movements for observation and study, amplifying time as loud-speakers do sound. Thus movement which ordinarily escapes the eye can be seen, just as ordinarily inaudible sounds can be heard when picked up by a microphone and broadcast by a loud-speaker. Still-camera photography can pick out and preserve the happening of a thousandth of a second or less. And the perceptions of cameras are infallible; they record what actually occurred. Hence, modern observers of bird flight, while they might err in their interpretations of the meanings of wing and tail positions, do not have to rely on their recollections of mental images recorded by eye.

Hence, with the facilities now available, aided by the developments of Lord Kelvin's successors, one of the mysteries which Solomon could not fathom need not puzzle us. Though we may still wonder about bird flight, we can understand this supreme achievement of nature; we may even climb aboard an airplane and simulate it. Furthermore, while we have been considering the whole subject, we are fortunate again in our own particular one—ducks—wherein nature has evolved a fascinating, harmonious blend of many avian extremes.

In size and shape, ducks strike a versatile median between the large, ungainly birds of remote areas and the insignificant chirping birds of urban parks. Neither almost wholly aquatic like loons, nor almost wholly terrestrial like partridges, ducks share parts of the lives of both. Compared to the exotic perching birds, ducks' colorations are modest; yet they do not look drab and sombre like some birds of the forest floor. Even their long migrations appear moderate when compared to those of species which fly from one hemisphere to the other, or to the arctic tern, which migrates from the Arctic to the Antarctic.

And duck wings, too, seem to blend the characteristics of those found at either ends of several scales. Their area compared to body weight is a compromise between the extremes. Some hummingbirds, for instance, have approximately ten times more wing area for each unit of body weight than loons. Duck ratios come in between. But the ratio for river ducks is much higher than that for diving ducks, whose low ratio may be one of the reasons they must run upwind to take off in flight.

Teal, shovellers, and wood ducks have about one square centimeter of wing area for each gram of weight, whereas scaups have only two-fifths as much and old-squaws still less. Mallards', black ducks', and pintails' ratios strike an approximate average for the whole duck family—about three-quarters of a square centimeter of wing area for each gram of body weight.*

There does not seem to be any relationship, however, between these ratios and air speed because of other factors involved; rapidity of wingbeats and their amplitudes obviously play an important part in speed also. Nevertheless, it is interesting to note that teal and wood ducks, having rapid wingbeats and high wing ratios, are among the fastest fliers of the duck family.

In other respects, too, one notes the absence of excesses in duck wings. Their camber is not exaggerated like that of the stubby wings of wild turkey and quail, whose flights are short. In shape they have no aberrations like those of some soaring birds such as the albatross, whose long-armboned, five-foot wings may be only nine inches wide. Yet duck wings have strength for long, sustained flight. They are capable also of reasonably sharp turns, soaring for short distances, and swift motion. They are indeed versatile instruments.

And because of their wings, ducks are among the most fortunate of beings. To them distance, the enemy of most members of the animal kingdom, presents no obstacles. They can escape fire, drought, famine, and chill weather. With equal facility, they traverse lofty, snow-mantled peaks and vast stretches of parched wastes. They cross with ease yawning chasms and quagmires, foaming rivers, and inland seas; they sweep over hazardous crags and precipices and boggy swamps faster than the fleetest deer can bound over level prairie. Their one great misfortune, it seems, is that their flesh is tasty to man. Otherwise, ducks certainly are favored creatures, so provided that they themselves need never want for food or water or temperate weather.

*E. A. Poole. See page 249 for his table of ratios.

One might assume they inspired Milton to write—
> *"Divinity within them breeding wings*
> *Wherewith to scorn the earth."*

* * *

On the following pages are several photographic series illustrating the duck's use of wings in the various types of flight we have been discussing. Richard Bishop accompanies them with interpretive sketches and comment.

Top of the up beat.
Wings almost parallel.
Tips over tail.
Wrist
Elbow

Partway down.
Breast muscle bulging with effort of pulling wing down.

Keel divides breast muscles

Tail depressed.

Wings continue down and forward.

Nearing bottom of down beat and turning away.

Elbow

page 114

Wing tips as far forward as bill at end of down stroke.

up beat has begun with raising of elbow and wrist

Primaries open to allow easier start of upbeat.

Starting last part of up-beat.

Last part of the up-beat

wrist.

Elbow.

page 115

The forward beat of the wings hits the air which spreads in various directions over the under wing area causing covert feathers to be blown out of place.

also bends the primaries back.

Coverts out of place

A partial vacuum is created on the recovery stroke on the under side of the wings which also displaces the covert feathers.

Some hens have very dark neck feathers which at a distance makes them look like drakes.

Front edges leading

Just after the start of the down beat in hovering flight. Horizontal wing beat.

Wing tips are on same level at start and finish of beat.

Just after the start of the up beat. Primaries are being separated from the secondaries and will be twisted by the wrist joint almost bottom side up as the up beat progresses.

Wings at end of forward beat. Wing tips ahead of bill. Tail cupped.

Wrists up first. →

Primaries seperated to allow air to slip thru during start of recovery stroke.

Has swung body to the left, selecting a different spot to "land".

Beginning of forward stroke with wing tips almost touching well behind tail.

Turns head and take a look at the blind.

Way off balance but using feet and extra pressure on right wing to recover.

Broken pinion

Ruffling of feathers due to partial vacuum.

The extra pressure on the right wing is swinging the body back.

Wing section same as airplane wing section.

This part of the stroke gives the air a backward push which helps to give a continuous forward motion.

Broken pinion

Start of the down or forward wing beat. which is almost horizontal

Wings half way on the down beat. Forward edges depressed.

Wings all the way
forward at end of
down beat.

Tail depressed and
spread to act as a brake.

Feet out and
spread like
snowshoes.

Half way back on the
recovery or up stroke.

Primaries twisted upside
down as wings are
jerked back.

Feet are swung backward and forward with each wing beat to help maintain balance.

The leading edges of the wings are depressed.

Wing tips almost touch at extreme top of up beat.

He has difficulty seeing downward over his crop full of rice.

Feet back.

Half way thru the down beat.

Feet forward

As the wings are snapped back the primaries are separated from the secondaries. The primaries are turned upside down by twisting the "wrist" and are bent at the ends by the powerful up beat.

Feet forward.
Tail depressed.

Half way thru the up beat.

Wing tips almost touch at extreme bottom of down beat.

Feet back.

These pictures are from the same sequence but are not in series

Looking like a throw-back to his reptilian ancestors, this drake's primaries take on a claw-like appearance as they bend sharply at the beginning of a quick recovery stroke.

Casting off the illusion of atavism, the primaries' dark edges, during the recovery stroke, are accentuated by the sun.

page 124

In ascending flight, shoulders move forward and wings assume an advanced position. As they pull the wings down, the pectoral muscles bulge over his keel. Although a duck's skin is firmly attached to the keel, the pectoral muscles, having no attachment whatever to the skin, work under it freely.

In slow pitching or ascending flight, feet and tail usually keep time to wingbeat. At the beginning of the downstroke, feet are forward and tail slightly elevated.

Start Of Down-Beat

The next four pages show one complete wingbeat. almost the only time a duck tips its head out of level is when selecting a place to pitch.

Tip of the wings are back over tail and feet forward.

Wrist

Elbow

Right wing

Winglet →

Right Wing

Tail open

Wings about one third of way down and tips of wings over legs. The tail has moved down and the feet start back.

Down-Beat Continued.

Most of the effort of the wings is going into the support of the body against the action of gravity.

Wing tips are now over the shoulders.

As the downstroke proceeds, feet move backward . . . and as it is almost completed, tail is depressed, catching the rush of air from the wings, tending to hold up the after part of the body and maintain balance.

Wing tips are well forward of the bill.

The tail is depressed and cupped.

The feet are well back of the position shown at the top of the opposite page.

End of the Down-Beat and Start of the Up.

This shows the extreme forward position of the wings. Tail depressed and feet back.

Note shadow of head on wing.

These photographs were selected from a sequence, to illustrate the various positions of wings during a pitching wingbeat cycle. However, they are not from a single cycle.

On recovery or up beat the wrists are raised first. During this part of the stroke the primaries are opened like a Venetian blind to decrease air resistance.

End of the Up-Beat

The primaries are forced quickly backwards giving a forward push.

Each open primary acts as an airfoil.

The secondaries being close to the body are not effective.

As the recovery stroke is almost completed, the tail is being elevated again and the feet are moving forward.

Winglet
Right wing

Recovery stroke or up-beat is nearly completed. The opened winglets show very plainly under the wing as well as on the left wing.

Looking sideways and beginning the down-beat. Feet thrown to right to aid in turning left.

Shadows of right wing primaries

Has lowered head to select a landing site. Down-beat ends - wings straight ahead.

The up-beat is started by raising wrists.

(These pictures are spot-shots of several series.)

wrists are almost touching.

The back flip of the primaries during this part of the stroke helps maintain forward motion..

The "Venetian blind" effect allows air to pass freely thru the pinions

↑ Damaged wing

By hitting branches as they fly thru the timber, their wings are frequently damaged!

Bad ↙ wing.

Bad wing probably keep this duck off balance.

Down beat starts. Pectoral muscle bulges in the effort.

page 131

The problem of where to land is being debated in this drake's mind.

While his wings beat in a horizontal plane, his head tips sharply forward to see what is below. Recovery stroke almost complete.

Damaged pinion

Sees something to avoid when pitching and turns to his left to avoid it. Starting the down stroke.

He decides on a patch of water nearer the camera.

The axillary feathers fill in and streamline the juncture of the wing with the body. Also shown in photo on opposite page.

Still turning more to his left, as the wings are about 3/4 thru the up-beat.

page 133

Wings almost touching and parallel as the down-beat starts. The feet are almost touching and pulled back. Tail fanned almost 180 degrees.

Hovering over a patch of water before deciding to pitch in.

Half way thru the down-beat. The feet are spread and pushed forward.

Wings in extreme forward position and tips almost touching. Tail is cupped and well forward.

Right wing beating higher than left, probably to straighten himself out, as it would tend to pull the upper part of his body in that direction.

Wrists are almost touching as up-beat is about half accomplished. Has opened one paddle. He now drops almost vertically into the small water area.

Thousands of muscles take part in the complexities of wing folding.

Axillaries closing angle between wing and body.

Puts more pressure on left wing to force body to her right to avoid hitting drake.

Start of recovery stroke.

Primaries open to ease return.

Wings touching

Axillaries

3 Point landing almost.

Off balance as she hits the water caused by change in direction to avoid hitting the drake.

This wing lower than other.

Head turned to the right.

Getting ready to fold wings

Primaries + Secondaries starting to separate.

page 136

Wave started by body

wrist

Side feathers are raised and the wrist is tucked under them.

Primary feathers are folded and slipped under the secondaries. That is why the speculum shows when the wings are folded when swimming..

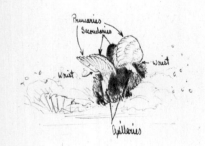

Primaries
Secondaries

Wrist   Wrist

Galleries

How They Do It

Dick Bishop often comments that, although thousands of gunnermen have watched millions of ducks fold their wings, few know what takes place. So fast is the process accomplished that, in the accompanying series, only a fraction of a second is required for the operation. Yet is quite a complicated procedure requiring the instantaneous coordination of thousands of muscles.

As outlined in the sketches below, the primaries (1) slide under the secondaries (2), which in turn slide under the tertials (3). Simultaneously and in a similar manner, individual feathers in each of these feather areas slide one under the other, just like an old-fashioned ivory fan; i. e., the first (outermost) primary slides under the second primary, the first (outermost) secondary slides under the second secondary, and so on. Thus, when the wing is folded the feather nearest the body is the first primary.

As the wing is brought down, the side body feathers are raised and the wrist is tucked under them. (See Sketch B and photograph and sketch at the top of this page.) When folding is completed, these side feathers cover the edges of both primaries and secondaries but leave part of the speculum showing. (See Sketch D.) The wings are so shaped that they conform perfectly to the curvature of the duck's back.

This process is reversed when wings are opened.

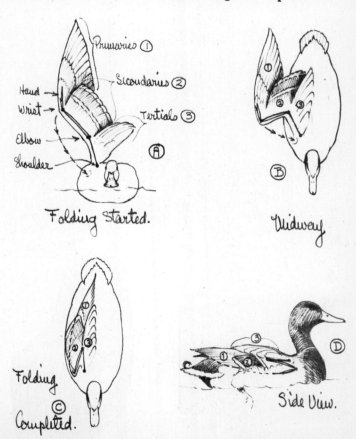

Spotlighted

All-Purpose Tails _____

THE tail section of a duck serves many purposes. Not only does it complete the streamlined shape of the body when the tail feathers are folded, but also these feathers form an effective airfoil when fanned out. It is a most flexible one; its angle of attack can be varied, the whole of it may be shifted from side to side or twisted; or one side of it may be folded while the other remains open. Consequently it is employed continually as a stabilizer. It is also used in an auxiliary fashion as a brake or wing flap, a rudder, and an elevator. Often it fulfills more than one of these functions at the same instant.

In comparison with some other birds, ducks have relatively short tails, and the ratio of the surface area of their tail feathers when fanned out, compared to body weight, is relatively small. F. W. Headley's tables indicate that this ratio in a sparrow hawk is about ten times that of a wild duck. Consequently the former are capable of making very much quicker turns. They and many other species are more agile in the air than ducks.

That ducks rely on their wings for most maneuvers is indicated by their ability to fly without apparent difficulty when their tail feathers have been removed. During a recent shoot with Dick Bishop, he brought down a mallard drake all of whose tail feathers and tail coverts had apparently been shot off or had been pulled off by some predator sometime previously, the tail section being com-

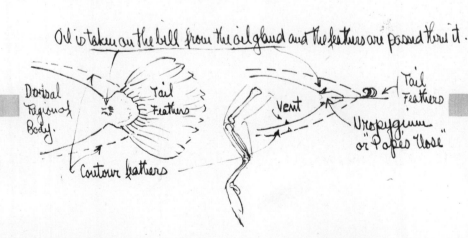

pletely covered with new pin feathers. This duck had been flying with several others, with whom it had no difficulty maintaining pace and direction.

Nevertheless, photographs indicate that ducks, particularly river ducks, utilize their tail sections constantly as auxiliary controls. They seem to be very useful appendages.

As indicated in sketches of a duck's tail section at the bottom of this page, the tail feathers project from the heart-shaped edge of the *uropygium*. This salient, commonly known as the "Pope's Nose," contains innumerable tiny muscles capable of moving and twisting it, as well as the tail feathers, in almost any direction.

In cruising flight the tail feathers are folded tightly, forming the termination of a perfectly streamlined fuselage; and the air stream slips over the body and the rather voluminous contour feathers of the tail section, then over the tail coverts, and comes together after passing over the tail feathers' tenuous tips.

When fanned out, the edges formed by the tails of different species vary, providing identifying field marks. The tips of a mallard's tail feathers, for instance, form a rounded edge; a wood duck's is somewhat square-shaped. In the case of a sprig, whose tail feathers themselves are pointed, it narrows into a mere pinpoint, which has named this duck; one calls it a *pintail*. Diving ducks' tails are so short that in flight their legs protrude beyond their tips.

In all positions except straight, level flight the tail is quite active, particularly in gusty air. Its chief function seems to be that of a stabilizer. A wild duck

In straight flight tail feathers are closed at the tip.

When changing elevation they are opened like a fan.

Fig. 1. *Low angle of attack . . . flap depressed.*

has a comparatively long neck, and the extension or retraction of his head is his chief means of controlling his center of gravity, but his tail is also instrumental for this purpose. The mere opening of it, even though its plane is kept in the neutral position, provides an additional airfoil on the after part of the body, moving the center of air forces backward.

The surface formed by extended tail feathers can be arched into a convex form or it may be curved downward and made concave. In these cases the drag resulting from the air stream slows forward movement and stabilizes the flight. To slow forward movement quickly, the tail is dropped. In this position it has the same effect as a lowered wing flap on an airplane (Figure 1). For very quick stops and descent, it is often cupped into a parachute-like form, providing a very effective brake. In gusty air and in descent, it is frequently shifted from side to side, thus aiding in maintaining balance.

If the tail's plane is raised or lowered, the after body section is correspondingly depressed or elevated, and in consequence the direction of flight is altered, as the case may be, upward or downward. A deviation of this angle from neutral—one so slight as to be all but imperceptible, even in slow-motion movies—is capable of producing a change in the direction of flight.

In the belief that a comparison with airplanes might be useful in gauging the amount of this movement, Glenn Martin offers this observation: "The ex-

To act as a brake, the
tail is opened and dropped.

To turn, it is twisted.

treme angles to which airplane tail surfaces move vary somewhat with the design of the airplane. On modern, high-performance planes having a wide range between landing speed and high speed, small movable surfaces are used to angles as large as 25° from neutral. In the case of the elevator, large angles are used only for landing, and for the rudder, they are used only for maneuverability at very low speeds or in the event of engine failure in multi-engined airplanes. For almost all of *normal* flying, the movement of both the rudder and elevator may be only a matter of a *few* degrees."

A change of "a few" degrees in the angle of the tail of a duck in cruising flight would be difficult to perceive. And, like the airplane's elevator, large angles are used in landing.

The tail is used also to serve the same functions as the rudder of an airplane. When its plane is twisted, the air forces acting on its surfaces change the course of the duck's flight.

This brief description of tail functions, however, is a gross oversimplification. A duck desiring to change its course seldom uses its tail alone. Tails are used in close coordination with both wings and feet. All act together—and the wings usually play the predominant part.

There is much to be learned about the coordination of wings and tail in flight. Interpretations of photographs are necessarily mere assumptions based on aerodynamic elementals. In each case, only the bird itself really knew why tail, wings, and feet were in their particular positions and how much each was contributing to the course of its flight.

To stabilize flight, the tail can be made concave or convex.

As though playing shadows, the sun paints on his under wing a silhouette of his head.

A study of tail positions. Cruising slowly and searching for a landing, some tails are closed, others open; some twisted and some shifted to the right, some to the left.

The varied positions reveal each individual's maneuver. No tail, however, is dropped down, indicating that none of them is quite ready to land.

Nature's wing slots. By raising his thumbs while pitching, this drake increases the effective drag of his wings. Tail dropped and fanned out.

The sharp ends of sprigs' tails point the origin of the name "Pintails." They are field marks. Two of the drake's central tail feathers are long, black, and pointed, and in flight accentuate his elongated tail.

Tail arched and concave, to slow and steady flight.

Climbing and trimming with convex tail.

Concave.

Convex.

As she drops down thru the branches this hen flattens depresses and her tail

to help her over some hurdle.

Now over the obstacle she makes her tail concave and twists it slightly to the left as she

continues to drop in that direction.

She continues to drop with tail
still raised and concave but
straightened.

With a clear space ahead and near

she flattens her tail feathers again and
twists it to the right as she pitches.

Tribious Feet

NATURE designed a duck's legs and feet to serve it in all three elements in which it lives—land, sea, and air.

On land their long toes preserve balance, as ducks have only two legs instead of the four hoofed or short-toed legs of land animals. As a duck's legs protrude from the sides of its body, the relatively wide space separating them accounts for its awkward, side-to-side, swinging gait when walking.

In the water, the webbed feet serve as efficient paddles. Opened on back strokes the webs present a formidable surface for propulsion. When drawn forward between back strokes, toes close, webs fold neatly into a rounded, streamlined form offering a minimum of resistance, and the feet slip forward through the water easily.

During flight, when ducks are in their true element—the air—legs and feet are tucked neatly into their undertail coverts, much as a bomber's landing gear is retracted into its fuselage and wings. But when taking off, when changing direction, when sudden gusts are encountered, or when landing, legs and feet have important steering and balancing functions.

When legs are lowered and toes are spread apart, the webs present a surface of resistance to the air stream. Thus feet usually coordinate with wings and tail when a duck is changing the direction of its flight. This function is especially important to diving ducks possessing small tails, such as scaups and ringnecks. It seems that, in compensation for their small tails not only were these species given what for a diving duck is a high ratio of wing area to body weight, but their feet were enlarged.

In flight, legs and feet have important balancing functions, too. When extended to one side or the other they exert an unbalanced weight, tilting the body or righting it, as the situation requires. Occasionally this unbalance is reinforced by opening the webs.

Balancing.

Braking.

Interesting Uses of Feet.

Steering.

As a rudder.

Supplementing tail action.

As he comes in to land, his tail is twisted . . . .

and his feet are used to balance.

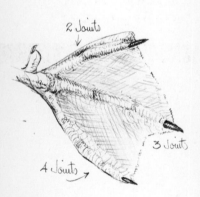

2 Joints

3 Joints

4 Joints

As he approaches the water, his feet are thrust forward

. . . and serve as brakes as he slides into the water.

All are in action as he

rounds this branch.

TAIL, WINGS AND FEET COORDINATING

This happened in a ¼ second, while nearing a tree top.

Raises and increases angle of attack.

Balances with her feet.

Head turned to see what's below.

Wings have different "angle of attack":

Increases angle of attack of left wing to help regain equilibrium.

In balance again

(Think she has had too many Martinis)

Holds right wing back

Advances left wing to turn away

Both feet and tail used in balancing.

She decides to make a sudden turn to avoid hitting a tree. Winglets are opened to act as air slots, tail opened and depressed simulating wing flaps, paddles spread for additional breaking.

Tail is coming forward and in lower picture forms with the wings one continuous airbrake surface.

Ludington recalls that, even after the turn of the century, lateral control of gliders "was achieved by the athletic prowess of the pilot who 'threw his weight about'."

This hen, pitching in gusty air, is throwing her weight about" to maintain her lateral stability. Her legs and tail section shift from side to side, acting as an unbalanced weight, thus offsetting the effect of an air current or checking an overcorrection.

That these shifts take place with incredible rapidity is indicated by the time interval between these photographs—one-sixteenth of a second.

Banking Ringneck

In appearance very similar to scaups, a ring-necked duck's distinguishing features are two bluish rings on the bill, a dark one at the tip and a broad, lighter one at the base; hence the colloquial name, *ringbill*. The rings are clearly visible in these photographs.

Ringnecks' flight, like that of scaups, is swift and their course seemingly erratic. Swishing through the air as they swerve quickly on their course, they tilt their bodies to one side then the other as they pass through branches and plunge heedlessly into decoys.

Without beating its wings during the maneuver, this ringneck banked to the right by changing its wings' angles of attack while balancing and aiding direction with its feet.

Coming straight on. Right foot out, balancing, left wing's angle of attack very slightly higher.

Looks to the right, angle of attack of both wings raised, tail dropped.

Left wing's angle now much higher; left foot drawn back, right foot braking:

The bank! Both feet drawn back out of air stream.

page 162

5

On its way. Elapsed time one-quarter second.

The Mewan Indians believed that ducks have webbed feet because the first duck to pass through the North Hole in the sky was not swift enough; the hole closed and the duck's feet were caught and flattened. Although their mythology speaks of a mallard, diving ducks, especially ringnecks and scaups, exhibit the greatest inheritance from the experience. As ringnecks and scaups have small tails, their enlarged, webbed feet take on added responsibility in balancing and steering.

page 163

Eight well-fed mallards arriving from a rice field. As the Grand Prairie is covered with rice fields, it was not necessary for them to fly far. Headley, however, cites an almost incredible instance of the distance ducks will go for food. He quotes "two highly competent observers" who reported that "ducks shot at dawn at Daimiel are found to be crop-full of rice. Now the nearest rice grounds are at Valencia, distant 180 miles; hence these ducks, not as a migratory effort, but merely as incidental to each night's food supply, have sped at least 360 miles between dusk and dawn." Quite a journey for a breakfast!

Clearing a tree top. Second drake from left, in order to rise, has opened his tail and changed his wings' angle of attack.

Ring-necked drake and his harem

A partial vacuum raises her wing coverts as she drops in.

High in the air, but he is coming in!

This pintail is in perfect aerodynamic balance. In quiet air he could coast down from the heavens without flexing a single muscle. It is apparent from the position of his eyes, as shown in this photograph, that he can see beneath his bill.

Miscellany!

Dick Bishop cautions: "Do not say, 'Ducks never do that.' Better say, 'Ducks seldom *do that*'." Odds and ends on the pages that follow include photochronographic and other bits of evidence that one would do well to heed his warning.

Ducks crash, too! Attempting too steep a bank, she stalled and fell in.

The wings are nearing the half-way point of the downbeat. Her head is turned to her right, where she plans to escape from the camera.

Ducks Must —

Learn to Fly.

This hen, raised in captivity, was released before the camera. Her awkward motions result from her struggle to gain command of the air.

Bishop has slow-motion pictures of the flight of young ducks, and observes: "All ducks must learn to fly. Their first attempts remind one of children's first faltering steps. It takes time and practice before they learn to handle themselves in the air like adults. My motion picture of a young pintail on South Carolina's Santee Delta contrasts its hesitating, rather groping flight with the assured wingbeat and balanced flight of an adult. Yet this young duck had already flown many, many hundreds of miles from its nesting grounds."

Near the end of the downbeat. Right wing gives an extra push to help her turn. Below: Recovery stroke has started.

Separation of the primaries shows on left wing. Legs are thrown out to help balance.

THE COURSE

● *Before photographs.*

◍ *From photographs.*

○ *Sketches from movies.*

Peeling Off

Early one morning Dick Bishop's ultra-slow movie camera and my Magic Eye camera were taking great advantage of frequent flights that were spotlighted by a brilliant sun. And as we were favored by a light southeast breeze, the birds pitched obligingly toward our blind and into the decoys.

After my films were developed, we found a sequence of a hen rolling over in reasonably good focus. But my camera had run down in the middle of her maneuver, just as she was on her back.

Later, when his movies had been developed, Bishop discovered that he, too, had photographed the same duck. His pictures revealed how she peeled off like a pursuit ship pulling out of formation, then dropped into the decoys.

Although obviously the maneuver had taken place before our eyes, the action was so fast neither of us had been aware of it.

But cameras cannot lie. And as each has its own constant speed, the maneuver could be timed by counting frames. My exposures were 1/16th of a second apart; Bishop's were 1/128th of a second apart. Therefore, the elapsed time between the first photograph reproduced in the following sequence and the last sketch was two seconds.

The approximate course of the maneuver and positions of the duck at the time of each photograph or sketch are indicated on the diagram above. Sketches were made from every twentieth slow-movie frame — intervals of 1/6th of a second.

PEELING OFF... *Photographs are from that part of the maneuver indicated by shaded ducks in the diagram.*

Having come in from the right, she decides on a change of direction.

Tail curved up at right, pulling with left wing.

Tail convex. Legs keeping time with wings.

Head is kept level. She looks for landing.

Left leg up; left wing working harder.

Tail is pushed to right.

Tail to left again.

4

5

6

7

8

Sketches of the positions assumed in Bishop's movie—that part of the maneuver indicated by outlined ducks in the diagram—illustrate how she dropped into the decoys.

The head is most revealing to follow. It points to the direction she intends to go. The tail, acting as stabilizer, rudder, and drag, swings almost 180° as she peels off, then drops down. Wings are brought into full play; feet aid in balancing. Elapsed time from photograph A to sketch 12 was two seconds.

1

2

3

9

10

11

12

Over!

page 173

1

2

Looking things over.

Opening the "winglets" creates a "slot" similar in action to the construction of the leading edge slots of some planes.

↓ *Note shadow of* ← *winglet*

Over Again _____

Although this sequence is similar to the preceding one, both are presented because such studies are so uncommon. Also, two series demonstrate better than one that birds actually *do fly upside down* for short periods, if, perchance, they fly into an unexpected air condition which unbalances them, or if they change their direction of flight very quickly.

The hen in this series was pitching toward my blind when she became aware of the sound of my camera. In her haste to get away, she turned herself over on her back.

The elapsed time between the first and last photograph of this series was 7/16ths of a second. Notice the changing position of her head, which turns around to the left —the direction she intends to take—before the body itself turns. In photograph No. 6, it is twisted 90° from its position in relation to the body in No. 1.

Her tail is used in this maneuver, also, swinging from one side to the other and twisting as it assists the wings make the turn.

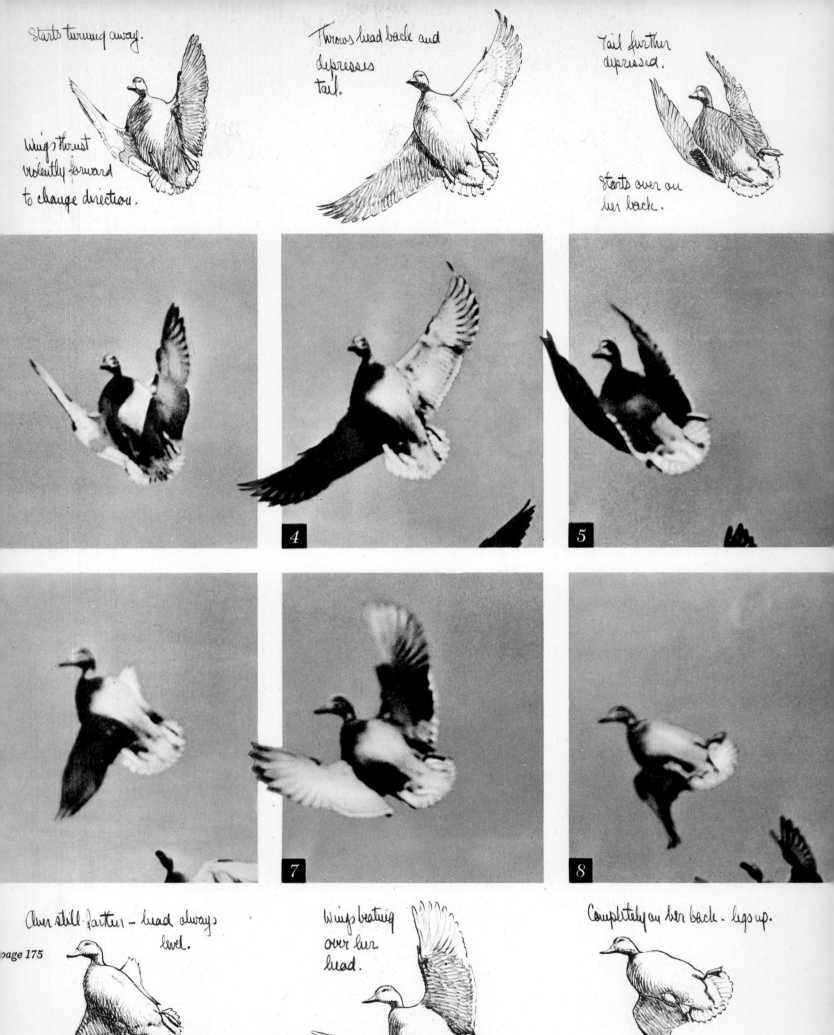

Starts turning away.

Wings thrust violently forward to change direction.

Throws head back and depresses tail.

Tail further depressed.

Starts over on her back.

4

5

7

8

page 175

Over still further — head always level.

Wings beating over her head.

Completely on her back — legs up.

Ducks can fly upside down!

GATHERING SPEED...*As she flies away, this hen demonstrates how, on a downbeat, the wings' leading edges are lower than their trailing edges.*

Primaries and secondaries are separated

Wrists

Primaries wide open

This drake seems to have unusually small feet.

HOUDINI . . . *This drake looks as though he is trying to climb out of his feathers. Actually, he is in the process of a recovery stroke while hovering over a patch of water, meditating whether or not to pitch into it. The lowering of his head shifted his center of gravity backward; hence he trimmed by drawing his tail forward, thus restoring balance. His ability to remain poised in such a position bears out Gordon Aymar's statement that "the portion of the ear devoted to equilibrium is highly developed in most birds." His tail feathers present an unusual aspect; not only are they fanned out, but each feather appears to be rotated like a turbine blade.*

VERTICAL GETAWAY . . . *The position of these pinions, at the end of a downbeat, indicates that a duck might "clap hands" behind its back. Pinions are straight down. Compare this angle with that of the wings on page 191 where, at the end of another downbeat, the primaries almost touch behind the head. The following pictures illustrate a vertical getaway.*

1

Out of the water, she starts her first recovery stroke.

At the end of the first recovery stroke, the tail is forward, for balance.

Another powerful downbeat. Wings are working forward now in a horizontal arc. Tail has been twitched back and is concave, tending to force lower part of body forward.

Up and up!

One eminent ornithologist has written that ducks are incapable of vertical flight; another that hummingbirds are the only birds able to fly backward. Here is the beginning, at least, of vertical flight. I have a slow-motion picture of a mallard rising vertically to the top of a hundred-foot tree. Then it flew backward some distance, turned itself around, and continued on in normal flight.

HAPPY LANDING . . . *Coming down into the wind, this drake has opened and dropped his tail, extended his feet forward, and scans an intended landing place.*

Satisfied, he raises his head, pushes back his tail.

Tail and feet hit the water at the same instant.

4

Holding wings back so they won't get wet, he inches in; momentum carries him forward.

5

6

Settled down, wings are folded neatly.

7

CRASH LANDING . . . *This old fellow strikes an unexpected air current.*

Balance lost and trying to right himself, feet are thrown to his right, tail is raised, left wing working vigorously.

2

3

His left wing still scooping air, he tries to regain balance.

Tail very high trying to lower after-part of body, he throws his right leg out to restore balance.

4

5

Recovers partly, but knows he is going to hit hard.

So, throwing his head up, he makes a belly-first landing.

6

7

He crashes in...decoy chides him.

Finale! Head almost under. Water covers body and wets wings.

While this drake was pitching in, he spied the camera...

and dropped one wing, so he could have a good look.

BAT DUCK . . . *With a vigorous downbeat, she is almost pulling her arm out of her right wing! The membrane leading from her body, forming the upper wing's forward edge, is clearly visible.*

SEMAPHORING? . . . *As she turns, her wings beat in different arcs and her right wing at a greater angle of attack. On the downstroke, wings assume the same position as that of a blue-jacket signalling the* annulling *sign.*

UNTIDY HEN . . . *The ruffed appearance of this hen is due to the partial vacuum caused by the reversed current when the air flow separates from her wings' upper surfaces. Scapulars have been raised, also, and cast a shadow on her body. The white feathers are axillaries which have been sucked up from below.*

NO FEATHER MAKE-UP USED! . . . *The edges of her primaries are naturally dark. In this position of the recovery stroke, we are looking at their under surface. The sunlight's angle accentuates this marking.*

DEVOUT HEN . . . *Primaries almost touching behind her head, simulating an attitude of prayer.*

FEATHER-DRESSER NEEDED ... *With wings at a very high angle of attack, a reversed air flow, as she drops in, rushes up both upper and lower surfaces of her wings, ruffling and displacing the coverts.*

SYLPH . . . *This slender duck is an immature pintail hen. Compare her pointed tail feathers with those of the mallard above.*

BALDPATE...*The white spot on this drake's head discloses the derivation of his name. In flight, baldpates — American widgeons — are readily identified by the flashing of the forewings' large white patches.*

BLACK DUCK . . . *Sex can't be determined from this photo, but if its bill was an orange-yellow it was a drake, if greenish-yellow a hen.*

THE PENGUIN

BALDPATE . . . *Balancing before dropping down.*

LEVEL HEAD . . . *When green-winged teal flash their white bellies, their bodies only have rotated. Their heads remain level and pointed in the direction of flight.*

THE AMERICAN EAGLE

OFF BALANCE . . . *She lost her poise when dodging the limb.*

SWAN DIVE? . . . *No! She is just swinging her wings in an arc parallel to the water's surface.*

SERRATED WING? . . . *The saw-toothed edge appearing to project from the tail is the right wing, the "teeth" being primaries that have been lifted up due to the air forces. Tail is dropped and slightly concave.*

ANSERINE SYNCOPATION . . . *This hen, flying on her side, proves that a duck's wingbeat is not always synchronized. Downbeat stroke of the right wing has been started; that of the left is midway.*

"Rollin' over in dawn's mist." As one approaches a raft, stragglers in the foreground rise, then pitch over the main body into the van.

Chapter Six _____

GUNNING ON THE GRAND PRAIRIE

Over the blind

FROM time immemorial the quest of birds has exhilarated man. Birds have also formed an important item of his diet. And as his mechanical arts progressed his pursuit of birds became more deadly.

It is not recorded how the wandering Israelites captured the flights of migrating "quail" that saved them from starvation. Some Egyptian friezes, however, which antedate Egypt's recorded history, picture men in marshes of the Nile snaring ducks with nets. And in the Middle Ages it was falconry; aerial retrievers captured flying game.

Dr. John C. Phillips noted that "when Penhallow visited the Kennebec River in Maine in August, 1717, he described a great duck drive during which 4,600 ducks were killed without the use of guns and afterward sold to the English for a penny a dozen." The method used by these Indians was probably the same as that witnessed by Audubon during his expedition to the Bay of Fundy a little more than a century ago. It was July. Drakes were in eclipse plumage and flightless. Some hens had moulted also. Audubon gives this graphic account:

"At the period when these poor birds are unfit for flight, troops of Indians make their appearance in light bark-canoes, paddled by their squaws and papooses. They form their flotilla into an extended curve, and drive before them the birds, not in silence, but with simultaneous horrific yells, at the same time beating the surface of the water with long poles and paddles. Terrified by the noise, the birds swim a long way before them, endeavoring to escape with all their might. The tide is high, every cove is filled, and into the one where we now are, thousands of Ducks are seen entering. The Indians have ceased to shout, and the canoes advance side by side. Time passes on, the tide swiftly recedes as it rose, and there are the birds left on the beach. See with what pleasure each wild inhabitant of the forest seizes his stick, the squaws and younglings following with similar weapons! Look at them rushing on their prey, falling on the disabled birds, and smashing them with their cudgels, until all are destroyed! In this manner upwards of five hundred wild fowls have often been procured in a few hours."

Ever since the colonists learned the Indians' methods and improved upon them, each generation has taken its toll of our wildfowl population. Until quite recently commercial hunters kept city markets supplied with great quantities of ducks. While Audubon stayed at a friend's plantation in eastern Florida one negro shot as many as 120 mallards a day, "thus supplying the plantation with excellent food." The much-prized wood ducks, he recorded, sold in South Carolina markets at thirty to forty cents a pair, and in Louisville, Kentucky, at twenty-five cents a pair.

Captain Bogardus' accounts indicate that he alone annually shipped several thousand brace from the Illinois River bottoms. The baited commercial slaughter pens operating along the Illinois River and on the Grand Prairie not long ago, where shifts of "sports" awaited their turn to take a guaranteed limit, were indeed no less gruesome than the Bay of Fundy hunt Audubon described.

But unlike other less fortunate game, which the increasing efficiency of firearms decimated, re-decimated, and in some cases exterminated, ducks have survived. Each spring they flew to northern potholes out of the reach of man and replenished, in part at least, the toll taken by hunters. Even so, the duck population became dangerously low a few years ago. However, with the return of favorable breeding weather, the inauguration of wise conservation measures, and the restoration of breeding grounds by state game commissions, the United States Fish and Wildlife Service, and *Ducks Unlimited,* ducks have exhibited a remarkable comeback. The increase has been noticeable in the bags taken in Arkansas' pin oak flats.

Duck shooting in Arkansas differs from that in any other part of America. Van Campen Heilner, in his thumbnail sketches of duck shooting in various parts of the world, describes shooting in pin oak flats as the fastest and most difficult of all.

I have seen men who rate as good shots in marshes go through two or three boxes of shells before pulling down their first limit from over the tree tops.

Sometimes one shoots from blinds, which are usually platforms nailed against trees and screened with curtains of leafy branches. But the most sport is had by wading into a flat, with a good native duck caller, until one finds an opening in the trees, and, while standing knee-deep in water alongside a trunk, enticing ducks into range by calling. In this case no decoys are used; the lure of the call is relied upon. And the fun of such a hunt is doubled if a good retriever is perched near by on a down tree.

On the Grand Prairie duck calling is both an art and an occupation. Duck calls are actually given to babies as teethers. As they grow up, youngsters practice with their calls, both in and out of season—and often with guns as well, to the despair of the local game wardens.

Stuttgart is in the heart of the Grand Prairie. Its Chamber of Commerce boasts, with more than the usual justification for Chamber of Commerce slogans, that "Stuttgart is the Duck Capital of the World." The night before the opening of each hunting season, Stuttgart holds a duck-calling contest for "The Championship of the World."

These contests are to Stuttgart what Mardi Gras is to New Orleans—the annual carnival. Contestants and farmers, men and women, from all the surrounding country gather on its streets. Hunting costumes of all descriptions are in evidence. And it seems that everyone's hat bears a disc—the Arkansas hunting license. The atmosphere is gay and jubilant.

One after another, contestants mount a platform erected on the town's principal thoroughfare and go through their repertoires of strident "open water" calls, succulent "feeding" calls, and lonely "mating" calls. Solemn judges of the art sit by an open window in the near-by Riceland Hotel, listen, and make notes to support their decisions.

One of the annual contestants, Jess Wilson, always receives an honorable mention but never first prize. He firmly believes that the contests are "fixed." Were this not so, he reasons, he would win. He "allows" himself to be "the best damned caller in the State." While I disagree with Jess' opinion that the contests are fixed, I disagree each year with the judges also, because I agree with Jess that he is "the best damned caller in the State."

I met Jess for the first time about ten years ago, when he was guiding near DeWitt on Elmer LaCott's Mill Bayou flats. The moment he stepped out of his tent to greet me, and before he had spoken a word, I knew I would like him, for there are silent voices between men also. A man's face is a chart of his soul. One look at Jess' face and I decided instantly that we would get along well together. I have shot with him ever since.

Jess is gaunt and of medium height. His inscrutable brown eyes look straight at you over high cheek bones and divert your attention from his prominent but well-shaped nose. His bronzed complexion and other aspects tell one that he is a product of the White River bottoms; that he has lived a rough life of hunting, trapping, and fishing. To say that Jess was not an educated man would be using the term in its narrow sense. It is true that, in common with the lot of river folk, he did not attend school. But the time missed at school was spent acquiring an education of which I am envious. Coming out of a lifetime in the woods, it is an education forever denied to most Americans of future generations. It is one that has fitted Jess for getting a living without the tools of "modern progress." Give him an ax and some matches and he can live; a gun and fishhooks would be helpful but not vital.

I think Jess must have a trace of Indian in him, for he has many of the traits which Father Membré, LaSalle's historian, ascribed to the Quapaw, or Arkansas, tribe. In contrasting the Arkansas with other Indians, Father Membré observed that the Quapaws were better made, gay, civil, liberal, and good-humored. Jess combines these qualities. He has a complacent, gracious, and retiring manner and a soft, pleasing voice. With women he is gentle, courteous, and most attentive.

When I introduce Jess to a friend, he appears somewhat perplexed, formal, and a bit uneasy. He remains silent but observes carefully, as though each man were made of doubtful gravel until panned out by himself. When fully satisfied, he warms up rapidly but never to the point of becoming effusive or garrulous.

His humor is reserved for those he knows well. When we are alone together, he voices his appreciation of the character of some of the men with whom he has hunted, while chuckling heartily over the human failings of others. He nails down a person's character unerringly. And at times he reveals himself as somewhat of an old rogue, delighting in petty, but never mean, advantages which he has taken of another's ignorance or inaptitude. However, most of his little tricks are wholesome.

For instance, I have seen him, when shooting with another man, kill a duck dead as a doornail while the other fellow missed. Then I've heard him burst out: "Yourn's kilt dead! I done missed mine cleaner'n a whistle!" And if the other accepted that verdict without protest, crows' feet would gather at the corners of Jess' eyes. He would scrupulously avoid looking at me for fear of bursting into laughter.

Many a novice who has shot with Jess came back with a limit, convinced that this timber shooting "isn't as hard as it's cracked up to be." Jess cajoled him with—"Ah've been a'huntin' hereabouts heaps but doggone if on your first timber hunt you ain't wipe mah eye shameful." Jess' speech is colorful and, Indian-like, is heavily weighted with similes and demonstrative pronouns.

Except when hunting, one might as well try to extract sunbeams from cucumbers as to get Jess to hurry. He would much rather spend an hour theorizing and speculating on a situation than a minute in pursuit of a solution. But this is a White River folk trait—and has merit, perhaps.

But when ducks are in the air and Jess dips his caller into the water to get it "limber-like" he has just one purpose in mind. He exercises laudable patience in achieving it and takes pride in his successes. If ducks are circling he is rigid. His eyes, skirting the brim of his hat, follow them intently. He may interrupt his calling for a single breath to murmur sotto voce, "Fixin' t' come in!" Then back to his luring. If he succeeds in bringing them in very close he may boast, "Dem critters come in wid dere tongues hangin' plum out!"

Jess has a large collection of calls. In addition to mallard calls that to me are indistinguishable from the real thing, he can make his duck call whistle like a pintail, squeal like a wood duck, crow like a rooster, and hiss like a hawk. With his mouth he can give a creditable imitation of a goose or a hoot owl and an all too realistic one of a screech owl. During interludes between flights he is always ready to give an exposition of his versatility. But if his caller is not in perfect tune he may exclaim, "Jesus whiz! Ah cain't call ducks 'less Ah sees 'em."

Jess' attitudes toward animal life present that paradox which I have noticed in many men who have spent a lifetime hunting and trapping. They exhibit at times an unsuspected sentiment and gentleness toward the birds and animals which it is their business to kill. I have watched Jess pick up a crippled duck, fondle it, and stroke its head with all the tenderness one might minister to an ailing child. He ascribes human emotions to ducks, deer, mink, and other animals. He often speaks of them and sometimes to them as though they were people.

It is said that the Indians used to address a reverential message to a moose or elk before loosening the arrow intended to kill it. And after the beast had fallen they served it with little favors such as placing it in a comfortable position and brushing snow off the dead face, in apology for their deed, before cutting it up.

Perhaps these traits derive from lonely years on the trail when animal life is the only company—when, too, an understanding of the lives and habits of the quarry is essential to outwit them and conclude a successful stalk. And it seems that with such understanding grows an appreciation of their sporting qualities, their family lives, and the tenacity with which they cling to life itself. The reaction may be the admiration one feels for an able adversary, intensified, perhaps after it has fallen, by the knowledge that after all the contest was an unequal one.

Jess' costume is ever the same: brown canvas hunting hat streaked with sweat and dirt, stained and tattered Duxback coat topping a flannel shirt, and brown hunting breeches tucked into black hip boots. Often these boots are patched; too often they leak.

At the end of each hunting season, when Jess is at the height of his prosperity, he makes a trip to town and buys a new outfit. By the time the next duck season opens, however, the months he has spent trapping for mink and fox and "head-lighting" at night for coon and possum have worn his outfit into its normal dilapidated aspect. But he is comfortable, usually dry, and disdains any suggestion that he discard his clothing in favor of some of mine.

* * *

One always remembers exceptionally fine hunts. Now I can recall many greenhead days, but my first will remain always a vivid recollection.

It was late in November. Nash Buckingham, Jess, and I were standing on the edge of a flat along Bayou LaGrue waiting for sunrise. We could hear the roar of an unusually large flight that had dropped in during the night. Jess noted, "The water's bilin' wid 'em." In view of the excellent prospects, Nash suggested that we make it a morning of greenheads.

When the sky began to pale, we waded in. My Labrador, Grouse, although his tail betrayed his pleasure of anticipation, restrained his eagerness and remained obediently at heel. We made our way carefully because the minimum penalty for tripping over a slippery, submerged log or stepping into a stump hole is a bootful of very cold water.

We could hear the ducks "rolling over" one another and the occasional roar as a wave of them took off in flight. Jess took due notice with—"Thar's a devilish swarm o' them buzzards ahead." Every now and then a near-by straggler startled us as it took to the air with a quack of alarm.

When we reached a likely opening in the trees, each of us leaned against a stump, Grouse took his usual stand on a partly submerged log, and we waited until sunrise.

The ducks we had stirred up seemed to fill the heavens. Their dark silhouettes, well in range, tempted us mightily. At sunrise the flight seemed to cease. Nevertheless, Jess dipped his call in the water to make it "limber-like" and began blowing some low, enticing notes. Occasionally he swished his boot back and forth in the water. This is an Arkansas trick; the resulting turbulence and waves in rapidly expanding, concentric rings simulate the appearance of the surface when ducks are about. When combined with calling, it proves an added and effective lure.

Soon a single came sailing over fully sixty yards high. Nash let go with the right barrel of his Long Tom. The duck folded up.

"Yuh shore did straighten him out, Mist' Nash," commented Jess, adding, as the duck splashed into the water with a thud a hundred yards away. "He dented that watuh fo' keeps."

At the word "fetch," Grouse leaped into the water and was off. But the duck was crippled. As Grouse approached, it dived. Grouse dived after it. Reappearing behind Grouse, it went off, broken wings paddling away the water at a terrific rate. After a long chase, however, Grouse overtook it. Then, with the cripple secure in his jaws, he puffed, blew, and snorted his way back to us.

It was the only duck to come within range for some time. Jess observed that they were "settin' down" on the far side of a near-by ridge. We decided to move there.

Nash was shooting his ten-pound, twelve-gauge Burt Becker bored double-barreled gun, whose thirty-two-inch, full-choke tubes have what he describes as a hose-like patterning power. He was loading with Western Cartridge's three-inch shell, packing one and three-eighths ounces of number four copper-coated pellets, which at that time was an experimental load.

We stood on the edge of the ridge, ankle-deep in the dank water. The ducks came over us as though Jess' call were a lodestone. Nash brought them down regularly at sixty yards—some we estimated, by using trees as yardsticks, to have been more than seventy yards away! Grouse had a happy and busy thirty minutes. Although Nash had his limit long before, at the end of that time we had ten greenheads apiece laid upon the bank. Then we sat on a log, lighted cigarettes, and watched. Ducks continued to pour in where we had been standing. Within the next hour we could have added many more limits without difficulty.

Such a day is exceptional. But when a flight is in a good pin oak flat, seldom is it necessary for even an average shot, once he is accustomed to the timber, to go home without his limit. Usually he has picked up his limit and is back in town before noon.

But at least half of the fun of a duck shoot is the company and work of a good retriever. I have been fortunate in having owned some splendid Labradors. One was outstanding; he captured my heart. It is still captive to the memory of Grouse of Arden.

And no record of my pleasures on the Grand Prairie would be complete without prominent mention of him.

Ducks circling overhead to Jess' call

Retrieving

Grouse of Arden

Chapter Seven _____

EXEMPLAR OF FIDELITY

TO GROUSE

Black, curly-headed symbol of devotion,
Of courage, strength and grace in every motion,
You bravely gave yourself in keenest measure
In daily service to your master's pleasure;
More constant in attachment than is woman,
More understanding than a fellow human;
Your loyalty spontaneous and unbought
And in return for which you asked for naught,
Not e'en sure food and shelter for your bed.
Enough for you, Old Boy, at workday's close,
With eager, pleading eyes and nudging nose,
To feel the gentle stroking of your head.
Sleep on in peace, in God's eternal plan,
Exemplar of fidelity to man.

STERLING E. EDMUNDS

Grouse and his master
(Courtesy St. Louis Post-Dispatch)

ONE of the bits that make Arthur Train's *Yankee Lawyer* such a delightful yarn is Ephraim Tutt's engaging little dog, "Chief Justice." Tutt lamented that had there been a Canine *Burke's Peerage,* "Chief Justice," or "C.J.," as Tutt affectionately called him, would not have been listed in it! He based his reasoning on the unknown ancestry of the little waif. It is my belief, however, that he allowed his love for "C.J." to lead him into the mistake of overprizing the merits of house dogs, and that he failed to recognize the true reasons for the truth of his conclusion.

It seems a certainty to me that all mention in such a Canine *Burke's Peerage* would have been pre-empted by sporting dogs! Furthermore, I am sure that most of the higher ranks of canine aristocracy, such as canine dukes and canine earls, would have been retrievers! For retrievers possess, in addition to the attributes of all other dogs, the qualifications requisite of chivalry—loyalty, courage, magnanimity, and quiet dignity. Only an occasional *declassé* among them ever shows his teeth, snarls, barks irascibly, or barks for the mere sake of barking. All retrievers true to type have that manner which among men marks gentlemen.

I admit to some prejudice because I have had some noble Labradors. Grouse, Shot, Nip, Tulle, and Sheena—all were aristocrats. Even Sheena's pups and Tulle's pups evidenced their blue blood at an early age. However, Grouse was the most illustrious by far.

Grouse certainly would have been in a Canine *Burke's Peerage!* His father was a British field trial champion and many others in his family tree were bench and field trial champions. I'm sure he could have traced his distinguished lineage back to the conquest of England's sportsmen by Labradors. I am certain, too, that Grouse would have appeared in the pages of an American Canine *Who's Who*. Many good judges of dogs who hunted with him would have written enthusiastic endorsements for his inclusion.

I met Grouse for the first time when he arrived after a long journey from an eastern kennel. As though impatient to get his first good noseful of Missouri air, he tried desperately to poke his truffle-like nose through the bars of his crate.

As soon as the crate was open, he bounded out and frisked in small circles and figures of eight, shaking himself vigorously. He stopped only to pay his respects to the nearest tree and for satisfying little sneezes. Then he rolled on the lawn, twisting and rubbing his back on dead leaves.

After these preliminaries he trotted over and looked up in an amiable way, as much as to say, "Well, let's get acquainted."

He sniffed at my legs and seemed pleased with my smells. I scratched his ears, ran my hands over his sleek ebony coat, and felt the ripples of lithe, firm muscle that lay beneath. And so began a friendship that ripened into a fast and lasting compact of allegiance. For four years Grouse was my constant companion.

Grouse was a fine-looking animal. He had a magnificent head, large expressive eyes the color of burnt sugar, a broad, deep chest, and a sleek, shining coat. But it was in the field and in the water that he excelled.

Scarcely had he passed his second birthday when his trainer entered him not only in the novice stake of a national field trial but in the open all-age as well, in which twenty of the nation's outstanding retrievers were competing.

Reporting on this trial, American dogdom's official mouthpiece, *The American Field*, said:

"Grouse of Arden, who placed second in the novice stakes, also placed fourth in the open all-age. Grouse again manifested ambition in his searching . . . He is a plucky performer . . . Grouse, a bold, industrious dog, marked his first cock well, made a credible find, a good carry and brisk return. He marked his second pheasant in this series beautifully . . . Grouse's marked retrieve of the duck was expertly accomplished . . . Grouse has a wealth of natural quality; he is a diligent hunter, gifted with a good nose and conspicuous perseverance. The dog's independence induces exercise of his own initiative rather than immediate response to signals, but the results achieved are beyond cavil."

The qualities which the author of this article attributed to Grouse as a novice remained his outstanding characteristics when he matured. But these were qualities of his field trial work. The author of the report had no opportunity to appraise him as a gun dog or companion.

Although I have great affection for dogs, I have always heartily disliked maudlin accounts of relationships between man and dog. Therefore I shall be factual. If my friends recognize any overstatements, they are due to the emphasis that Time has placed on those pleasant events and treasured relationships which cannot be recaptured or repeated.

Grouse and I were attached to each other by mutual esteem and affection. When walking he stayed at my heels like a shadow. At home he curled up beside my chair, his head between his outstretched forepaws, which it seemed he passed hours washing and washing and washing. When we motored out to a hunt he sat upright on the seat beside me, thoughtfully drinking in the passing scene and expressing his pleasure of anticipation by whacking his tail occasionally on the seat.

Often he slept beside my bed—sometimes in a trailer parked near an Arkansas pin oak flat, sometimes in a Pullman compartment, sometimes, when we hunted along the marshes of the Mississippi, in my room at the Cuivre Club.

He was an excellent roommate. Only at Cuivre Club did he ever wake me.

There, when he heard the morning fires being kindled, his tail would beat a tattoo on the floor. And if I did not stir, he could no longer restrain his eagerness to be about our business of the day. Jumping upon my bed, he would lick my hands and face as much as to say, "Wake up, old sleepy-head! Don't you know it's time to be up and at 'em?"

Cuivre Club's blinds are old hogsheads that have been sunk into the marsh, only six inches or so of their rims projecting above the surface. Grouse sat on a platform that hooked over the rims—a shaky and often a very cold perch. But he was never happier than when sitting there, alert but motionless, his eyes roving over the sky searching for any flights that might appear and following wistfully any that circled near us.

If ducks came in range and I missed, he merely raised an eyebrow. But two misses in succession provoked his disgust. He reproached me in no uncertain terms by a disdainful look and bored manner.

When a duck was down, however, Grouse's whole body quivered with excitement. At the word "fetch" he was off like a streak! He was a powerful swimmer. He put his whole body, even his tail, into his strokes, the force of which pushed his head and shoulders out of the water and left a more than perceptible wake in his course. Upon reaching the duck, one coordinated motion appeared to grab the duck and wheel Grouse about in readiness for his usual brisk return.

Climbing back on his platform, he often indulged in a good shake before handing the duck to me. Then he would sit down and resume his characteristic pose of watchfulness.

Nash Buckingham often shot with us in Arkansas. He became well acquainted with Grouse. Nash has spent half a century in the field; he has judged and shot over thousands of bird dogs and retrievers. In his enchanting book *Tattered Coat* he reminisces with tales of the greatest dogs he has known.

Out of this select company he chooses a mere handful to crown his *pin-up dogs*. With all the color characteristic of his writing, he tacks them up on his walls of fame, one by one, with narratives of their exploits.

My Wingmead Bill—an eager, willing setter whose future days afield, I fear, are now too few—hangs in the bird-dog room of this exclusive gallery. And on the walls of Nash's retriever room Grouse occupies the most prominent position. Here is his portrait of Grouse:

"One of the most interesting afternoons I have ever spent behind a retriever was during November, 1939, in a pin oak flat along Bayou LaGrue. Edgar, Dick Bishop and I, with Grouse of Arden, Edgar's magnificent black Labrador, were exploring new territory for some high timber shooting. Our canoes raised hundreds of mallards as we slipped along the bayou, spilling over its banks in spots.

"After finally going ashore, we waded through ankle-deep water to a long, narrow ridge that ended against a canebrake. Jess Wilson and Foy Dinsmore unlimbered their duck calls, and it soon became evident that great sport was in prospect. Grouse had comparatively little to do until, after a particularly lively volley, three cripples sailed through the timber beyond the canebrake and disappeared. They must have hit water in the flat woods down the bayou. Dick and Edgar attempted to wade around the canebrake, but a deep slough threatened their boot tops.

"I was using breast-high waders, however, and after some delicate stepping I made it across the 'dreen' and into a veritable far-flung fairyland of shallow water stretching away beneath low-hanging, sun-tinted foliage. Grouse swam across the deep chute, waited for me to land, and then, with a look that said 'I'll be seeing you again,' took off at a run through the backwater. Quartering against the breeze to catch the scent, the big black dog swung a half circle.

"I sat down on a chunk to watch the proceedings. After a bit I heard quite a fluttering down the line of the canebrake, and here came Grouse with a winged greenhead in his jaws. Handing it over, he whirled and struck a left oblique across the woods. I could hear him splashing a long way off, but he was lost to sight for a spell. Then he fetched in a dead hen mallard. Do you think Grouse didn't know that there were three ducks down? I had no direction to give him, and he didn't wait for orders. He was gone fully fifteen minutes that last cast, but returned with a badly crippled drake. Handing it to me gently, his eyes seemed to say, 'That's getting 'em, ain't it?'

"We rested a few moments while I gave him a taste of chocolate candy. Then we rejoined Edgar and Dick. It is well to inscribe such feats as that upon the pages of sporting lore."

Between hunting seasons Grouse relaxed and took on weight, passing the time curled up under the piano or stretched out beside my chair in our living room.

One spring day John Wallace, President of the Mississippi Valley Kennel Club, telephoned: "The Club is going to hold its first national retriever trial. We want some local dogs in it. Won't you enter Grouse?"

I had had no experience in field trial handling, but, as John promised to give me a brief course in the etiquette, I assented. Grouse must have overheard my conversation with John, because he eagerly gave up the comfort of the living room for a few rehearsals.

When again in competition, Grouse recalled his early training. It proved to be a case of the dog handling the handler. Grouse won the amateur all-age trial and placed third in the open all-age. He defeated many of the nation's best retrievers who had made field trials a career and who, with their professional handlers, had spent their lifetimes making circuits of field trials.

Later one of the judges confided that Grouse would have won the open all-age, also, had he not, in a series wherein two pheasants were shot, started retrieving the dead one and dropped it in order to go after the second, a crippled one, which was running away. While such a performance marks a good gun dog, it is taboo in field trials, their standards requiring that once a bird is picked up it be retrieved without interruption.

Thereafter Grouse and I entered several spring and fall trials that were held in St. Louis. Although we spent little time in preparation for them, not once did he fail to take honors.

If Grouse had had a master sufficiently interested in field trials and possessed of the necessary time to travel the circuits, it is evident that he would have achieved renown. In most of these trials he placed himself ahead of Field Trial Champion *Rip*, Paul Bakewell's glorious Golden Retriever, a dog of Grouse's age who subsequently won twice in succession the trophy which *Field and Stream* awards annually to the year's outstanding retriever.

I hesitate to relate the following incident because it sounds fanciful and my veracity might be questioned with fair cause. However, I vouch for its truth.

We were living in Arkansas at the time. One evening when I returned, my wife burst out, "You will never believe this one! Grouse pointed a covey of quail this afternoon! Both Kate and Bill overran it, but Grouse picked up the scent, trailed the covey, then nailed it down in the best bird-dog manner! I flushed it and knocked down a cock, then Grouse rushed out and retrieved it for me!"

The performance sounded like an accident. We had been losing quail. The ground had been dry and our setters, Kate and Bill, had failed to find and retrieve some birds that had been knocked down. Therefore, we had been taking Grouse on our quail hunts and he found well. But he disliked staying at heel while our setters were having all the fun of casting and quartering the fields. He broke often. It was obvious he disliked being called back.

Summing up the incident, my wife added, "Grouse acted just as though he were saying, 'If this is what you want done, it isn't necessary to take those setters with us at all!'"

I was very incredulous indeed. I determined to find out if he would repeat.

A pet, never-to-be-shot covey roosted near our lodge. The next morning I walked Grouse toward its roosting grounds and bade him—"Hunt, Grouse! Scurry around here! Find that covey!"

After a few minutes the miracle happened again! Grouse was on point, solid as a statue, head erect, one forepaw lifted and bent back, tail rigid and "all styled up," as they say in the south. It was hard to convince myself I was not dreaming. But there he was!

Shouting "Good old Grouse! Steady, boy! Hold it!," I walked toward him, gave him an approving pat, then flushed the birds. He seemed well pleased with himself.

I was happy too!

But we did not hunt quail again. A few days later we took our usual stand in the flats. It rained in heavy volleys. Shooting was poor. Grouse evidenced little interest in the hunt. He was listless. Retrieving the few ducks that were shot appeared a chore.

That night he lay on the rug before the living room fire, as was his wont when conscious of a good day's work well done. Often when lying so he had nightmares; or perhaps they were pleasant dreams. At any rate, he would emit soft whines and paddle away with his feet as scarcely audible "woofs" escaped from his lips. I could never determine whether a demon from canine purgatory was chasing him or he was on the hot trail of a crippled anserine goblin. But he manifested gratitude always when awakened. Then he would arise, stretch himself like a tiger, yawn mightily, roll his tongue around his chops, sneeze once or twice, and return himself prone on the rug. Laying his head on his outstretched legs in thoughtful repose, he would meditate upon whatever fantasy had passed through his mind.

But that night he did not whine. He moaned! As I knelt and patted him, his eyes poured out not only their usual affection but a piteous plea—"As you love me, help me! I have terrible hurts!"

Early the next morning I took him to Little Rock. After examining him, the veterinarian uttered two ominous words that haunt me still—"Ratbite fever."

Two days later the curtain fell; Grouse was dead!

*   *   *

Grouse did not take up with many people. Never hostile, he merely held himself aloof. He would submit with obvious indifference to the pats most people bestowed, then trot off and shake as though he would rid himself of unwelcome smells.

But there were exceptions. Many of my friends can converse with dog and tree in the voice of silence. Sterling E. Edmunds was such a man. He hunted with Grouse many times. They were good friends.

Sterling's ability with his pen matched his skill with his rod and gun. Upon learning that Grouse had taken the trail to the Land of Spirits, he promptly turned some phrases of silver into an elegiac sonnet. I treasure it for its beauty of expression, its graceful understanding of an exceptional dog, and because of the sentiment echoed in its last couplet:

>"Sleep on in peace, in God's eternal plan,
>Exemplar of fidelity to man."

Dick Bishop sketching in a pin oak flat

Chapter Eight _____

PLEASURES THRICE ENJOYED

Following the leader

B<small>EFORE</small> I discovered how many pleasures were latent in ducks, I thought of them as flying targets—something to be shot. The pleasure of a day in the blinds was measured largely by how often I held the correct lead. It was limited, too, by the Fish and Wildlife Service's ruling that one must not shoot more than a certain number.

Then, one evening, Dick Bishop projected on the screen his ultra-slow motion pictures of bird flight. For the first time, I saw how the graceful pintail rises from water. I noticed the delicate movements of a bird's body and wings in flight.

I was fascinated.

Although I had previously indulged in some wildlife photography, I now determined upon it in earnest.

Dick Bishop is a most generous person. He gladly shares with others the great store of lore he has accumulated during a lifetime's study of wildfowl. He gave me camera and lens data and many helpful hints. I soon became the captive of a new hobby.

Dick's paintings and etchings of wildfowl are outstanding because he is not only a superb artist but a topnotch engineer! As a result of his engineering training and his understanding of aerodynamics, mechanics of flight and the anatomy of birds came as second nature to him. This knowledge of anatomy and mechanics of flight is brought to the aid of his artistic concepts. The results are portraits of birds as they really fly! And I use the word *portrait* in its old sense—that of a vivid description of something living. So many etchings and paintings of game birds by other artists please the eye but are technically bad. These artists picture flight as they imagine it occurs.

It was not long before my new hobby revealed duck flight, which had provided only one pleasure, as the source of others. One pleasure soon became two, because I went to my blinds with gun *and* camera. I had two things to shoot with —and there was no legal limit to the number of pictures I might shoot. And now, when the day promises good light, I usually leave my gun in its rack, because there are pleasures enough with camera alone.

I often refer to my cameras as my *white stone canoes*. There is an old Chippewa legend that a fortunate member of the tribe was singled out by the Master of Life and provided with a white stone canoe in which to journey away from their Land of Snows to a Happy Island. He reached a paradise of green valleys, pleasant trees, and bright and sparkling streams, where there were no wars and no tempests—and there was no hunting because the very air itself was food. On this Happy Island, birds flew freely and animals, having no fear of bloodshed, bounded about the woodland with confidence.

But I fear the analogy I draw is not shared by ducks. They seem as wary of the motions and sounds made by a man with a camera as they are of those made by a man with a gun.

Ultra-slow motion pictures made with my Bishop-type "white stone canoe" prompted me to attempt freezing some particulars of duck flight in still pictures. In the quest for really good still pictures, however, more obstacles are encountered than in a steeplechase.

Robert Fisher, now a resident of photogenic Florida, initiated me into the mysteries of the darkroom and taught me about films, papers, and developers. He helped me build my darkroom, in which we carried out the considerable amount of research that was necessary in film and fine-grain developers before the goal was achieved.

Over a period of many years I experimented in duck blinds with cameras ranging from a sixty-pound, forty-inch Big Bertha Graflex to a gunstock-mounted Leica. In unsuccessful attempts to photograph ducks with stroboscopic light, I have sat in a blind hours on end, holding between my legs a condenser charged with 30,000 volts of electricity, the current being provided by a generator mounted in a station wagon parked on the bank.

My best results, however, have been achieved with a Magic Eye camera which the manufacturer, upon learning my purpose, tried to discourage me from buying. He protested that his product had never been used for wildlife photography and, due to the conditions under which I would have to use it, he doubted that I would be successful—and he was very nearly right!

Magic Eye cameras are thirty-five-millimeter motion picture cameras whose mechanisms are altered so that they produce sequences of still-pictures.

Because they are too heavy to hold in one's hand, they had always been mounted on tripods. But with the camera on this conventional mounting I was unable to follow a bird and keep it in focus. After weeks of unsuccessful attempts and trying several alternative schemes, I regretted not having taken the manufacturer's advice. I almost discarded my Magic Eye. But at last, by suspending it in a homemade base from a branch of a tree, I found I could get the necessary flexibility.

Most of the photographs of single ducks reproduced in this book were taken with my Magic Eye. Pictures such as those composing the series of ducks flying out of water are novel. They could have been taken only with a Magic Eye camera; therefore, I am certain this is the first time such pictures have been published. For those interested in technical details of the photographs, I have elaborated in the Addenda.

In camera hunting, I have found that the usual pleasures of a hunt are magnified. The pleasure of anticipation overlaps that of realization, for it extends through the development of films and the printing of enlargements—and dark-rooms know no limitations of season, time of day, or weather. Furthermore, the pleasure of retrospect is augmented by a visible record of the event.

For with these records I can enjoy forever the recollection of the fascinating movements of that group of swirling greenwings that darted in from nowhere, twisted in unison just short of the blind, then flared, white bellies up, and vanished almost before their appearance was registered in my mind. I can enjoy the spoonbill's inquisitive head cocked at an amusing angle or an unusual twist to her dexterous tail; or a whirling blackjack with his grotesque feet and leathery webs spread wide; or the pageantry of a wood duck with his exquisitely painted wings lifted with lordly grace.

All that is missing from the pleasure of retrospect is color, the third dimension, the swishing of air, and the fluttering music of wings.

But even as I note the absentees, the cycle of pleasures is completed; the pleasure of retrospect gives way to that of anticipation. I find myself looking forward to fall, when *Keewaydin*, keeper of the mystic northland, unleashes the Hunting Winds. Then the subjects themselves will return, spread their wings in benediction over their haven in the color-spotted flats, and rest and dabble in the solace of its tranquil waters—amidst the vast silence of its very vocal trees.

Redleg

Addenda _____

Pintails reconnoitering

Camera Notes

GOOD photographs of wildlife are the result of extraordinary good luck or a certain amount of skill, coupled with infinite patience and a good knowledge of the quarry. For this reason wildlife photography will always remain the sole province of the enthusiast. The time element alone will exclude the professional; costs would be prohibitive.

For instance, over a period of years I have spent the equivalent of weeks attempting to get a photograph of a large mass of ducks that would approach in quality the extraordinary pictures made on Wilcox Lake. I threatened, if successful, to caption the picture as "made with the longest exposure on record"— the reference to exposure relating strictly to my person. Although at times my blinds have been surrounded by thousands and thousands of ducks, I have achieved no result worthy of reproduction in this volume. Without fail, the "raft" of ducks moved either too far away from the blind or into the wrong position relative to the sun.

In addition to an ample flight, a wildfowl photographer needs elements unessential to a gunner: good sun and the right kind of wind. The Grand Prairie's large flight usually takes place during the half-hours before and after sunrise, when light is insufficient for photography. As day unwinds the flight diminishes; at eleven o'clock it all but ceases. Even on a very clear day one cannot begin photographing successfully until eight o'clock suntime, when the peak of the flight has passed. Most of my pictures have been made between eight and ten in the morning.

The most attractive duck pictures are of incoming ducks flying toward the camera at low altitude. This requires, during the morning hours, a southeast wind. However, in Arkansas a southeast wind is the forerunner of rain. After it blows for a few hours, haze gathers over the sun and soon the sky is overcast. When this process is taking place, Jess is prone to remark, "Th' sun shore is puttin' on uh thik coat!"

The coincidence of a good flight, brilliant sun, and an early-morning southeast wind occurs infrequently. One season it happened but three times. However, within those few hours, I secured nine-tenths of my year's successful photographs. On one of these days, a film of ice covered the water, the only open spot being the patch Jess had cleared around the blind Dick and Helen Bishop and I were using. Dick was taking slow-motion pictures. Attracted by the open water, ducks poured in, providing a photographic field day for both of us. Two hours of that morning furnished three-quarters of my season's picture bag.

A variety of both cameras and films was used to make the photographs in this volume. Those of groups of ducks were made on 4x5-inch film with either a Baby Bertha Graflex mounting a 20-inch Dallmeyer lens, or a Speed Graphic mounting some days a 12-inch Dallmeyer lens and other days a 5¼-inch Zeiss lens. The films, usually cut films, were Agfa Superpan Press, Eastman Super XX, Panchro Press Type B, and since its recent introduction Panchro Press Sports Type. They were exposed for either 1/800th or 1/1000th of a second, usually at F-5.6 or F-8. However, the scene of several ducks pitching over the blind into the decoys, appearing on page 198, which I consider my best result, was made with the 5¼-inch lens on Sports Type film at 1/800th at F-16.

Four-by-five-inch films present no problems of development or enlargement. I usually use the developer recommended by the manufacturer for his product or Edwal 12.

All of the sequences and most of the photographs of single ducks were made with a Magic Eye camera mounting either a 17-inch F-4.5 Dallmeyer lens, an

11-inch F-5.6 Taylor-Hobson Cooke lens, a 6-inch F-2.3 Astropan, or a 6-inch F-2.7 Bausch and Lomb Baltar lens. Incidentally, Mr. Thomas J. Walsh, senior partner of the National Cine Laboratories, manufacturers of Magic Eye cameras, informs me that he knows of no other instances in which his cameras have been used for wildlife photography.

In most cases, the exposure was 1/1000th of a second, which usually "stops" all motion except that of wing tips. But a few photographs and the sequence beginning on page 42 were made at 1/2000th of a second.

As a Magic Eye frame is only ¾-inch high and 1-inch wide, the type of film to be used and its development presented problems. The over-all length of out-stretched mallards, from the end of the bill to the tip of the tail, averages 23 inches. As photographic objects, ducks in flight are not outstretched; furthermore, they are usually viewed at an angle, which further reduces over-all length. However, even a two-foot object 50 feet distant, when photographed with a 6-inch lens, produces but a ¼-inch image; and at 30 feet the image is only 4/10-inch. Hence, the production of a negative capable of substantial enlargement was an essential.

Short exposures are necessary to "stop" flight. However, a fast film such as Super XX is inherently grainy; thus when enlarged many times, prints made from it have a disagreeable, mottled appearance. A fine-grained film such as Panatomic X or Finopan, however, is slow, requiring several times the exposure of a fast film for equivalent register. Developers designed to fine-grain film reduce film speed; hence the most desirable characteristic of fast film is partly sacrificed, when fine-grained, in development.

Therefore over a period of years I attempted to ascertain the most suitable film and conditions for development. This volume contains representatives of many such trials: Agfa's Superspeed, Superpan Supreme, and Finopan, as well as

Eastman's Panotomic X and Super XX. I have tried all fine-grain developers recommended by Agfa and Eastman; also many others, such as Champlain's formulas.

The best over-all results were achieved with Super XX exposed for 1/1000th of a second at between F-2.3 and F-4.5 and developed in Edwal 20. Better contrast was secured with a three- to five-minute overdevelopment, adding to the developer a few drops of a wetting agent such as Santomerse S.

Using this combination, I have been able to make grain-free enlargements of thirty diameters, a portion of the tiny ¾"x1" negative making a good 16"x20" print even on glossy paper. Most of the series and most of the better photographs of single ducks were made in this manner.

If 1/1000th-of-a-second exposures were made on Super XX at F-4.5 under ideal conditions, development in Edwal 12 produced negatives making satisfactory enlargements up to twelve or fifteen diameters. My best results with Edwal 12 were obtained by following one of the methods recommended by E. P. Lowe in his book, *What You Want to Know about Developers*. I changed the formulation as follows: Glycin cut to four grams per liter, adding one-half gram per liter of potassium thiocyanate, diluting the solution 9:1 and doubling developing time.

My objective has been photographs on which, figuratively, "feathers could be counted," and which would also show some detail in shadow areas. Those approaching closest to this goal were made with the 6-inch lens at an F-2.3 aperture, the ducks being between 30 and 40 feet away.

But the depth of the sharp focus field at this aperture and distance is very shallow and that of critical focus even shallower.

Hence many sequences of ducks passing through the field of sharp focus have contained only one sharp, usable negative. So critical is this depth of focus that in some of the photographs in this book one wing is in sharp focus and the other out of focus.

As I usually start my Magic Eye photographing any duck I think will fly into the sharp focus range, the ratio of sharp frames to those exposed is very low. On a few happy occasions a duck flying across my decoys on a course perpendicular to a line drawn from me to the sun—and, therefore, well lighted—stayed in the field of sharp focus half a second or more and good sequences resulted. Sometimes, however, a whole reel of 1,200 individual negatives did not yield a single frame worthy of retention.

Certainly I have used more than fifty 100-foot reels of Magic Eye film during the past five years. Even fifty would have produced 60,000 individual negatives; yet, I have only a few hundred good ones and but a few dozen approached my goal.

And the best of these are reproduced in this volume.

The green-winged teal (page 28) and the wood duck (page 77) were domesticated, full-winged ducks reared on the author's pond in Missouri. All other photographs, except where specifically stated to the contrary, were made, by the author, of wild ducks in natural flight. The gadwalls (page 29) and coots (page 48) were photographed in Saskatchewan, the canvasbacks (page 49) in Manitoba. All other photographs were made in Arkansas.

The photograph *Evening Flight* (page XII) is an overprint. In *Above the Pin Oaks* (page 23) and *Eight Well-fed Mallards* (page 164) one bird in each negative was "moved" in printing to improve balance. *Rollin' Over in Dawn's Mist* (page 196) was printed through a fog filter. In *Following the Leader* (page 224) two birds not in the original negative were printed in. In no other cases were photographic artifices used.

The paratrooper

Rudiments of Flight *by* GLENN L. MARTIN_____

THE flapping flight of a bird in calm air is not easily explained; it is quite involved, because of many variables. The important variables are:

1. The angle of attack of various sections of the wing with respect to the bird's flight path;

2. The number of wingbeats per second, and the speed of the bird;

3. The time ratio between the downstroke and recovery.

Motion pictures of bird flight taken by a camera which swings with the bird in flight convey the impression that a bird's wing moves forward and down, backward and up. That is actually the motion of the wing with respect to the bird's body, but not the motion relative to the ground, or, more important, relative to the air. In almost all steady flight conditions, the wing of a duck advances forward through the air. On the forward and downward beat, the air flow over the wing is greater and the angle of the wing is flatter than on the backward recovery stroke, in which case the angle of the wing is steeper and the air flow is less.

However, if we assume that the bird's path in flapping flight is horizontal and in so-called "cruising flight," we can represent the path of a section of the outer wing by a curve as shown in Figure 1.

Fig. 1.

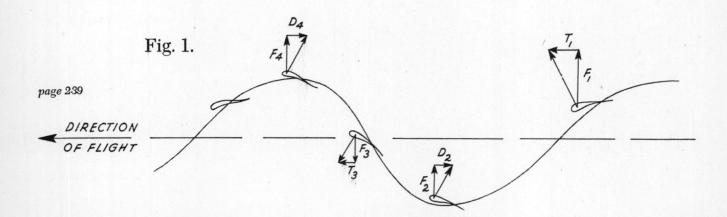

DIRECTION
OF FLIGHT

The sum of the forces $(F_1+F_2+F_3+F_4)$ over such a cycle must be equal to the bird's weight. If the bird is maintaining steady "cruising flight" i.e., not attempting to accelerate—the wing must be controlled so that the sum of the thrusting forces (T_1+T_3) is equal to the sum of the resisting forces (D_2+D_4).

This diagram can be seen to explain why photographs show the leading edge of a bird's wing lower than the trailing edge during the downstroke.

When the speed of flight of a duck is not adequate to produce the proper lifting force by vertical flapping, the duck increases the speed of the beat and moves its wings forward and down on the first part of the stroke to increase the speed of air passage over the wing. On the recovery stroke, the quick backward flip of the outer wing fingers relative to the bird makes it possible to increase the length of time for the downward stroke in any given beat.

Actually, a bird utilizes its strong inner wing for most of the supporting force, and causes the outer wing to move in accordance with Figure 1 in order to provide the propelling force. In that case, the sum of $(F_1+F_2+F_3+F_4)$ may be nearly zero, but the speed of flight causes the inner wing, which is relatively fixed like that of an airplane, to support the full weight of the bird as in Figure 2.

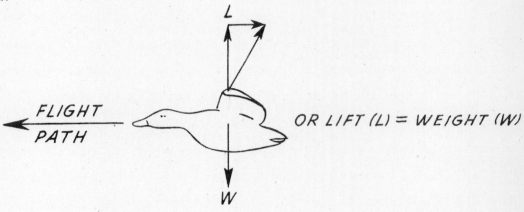

Fig. 2.

Gleanings from Authorities _____

THERE are many excellent non-technical books on the origin, life, habits, and flight of birds. For those whom this volume may stimulate into a further perusal of the subject, I have appended a small bibliography of what I believe to be the best that have come to my attention. I feel on very safe ground in promising any gunner that the pleasure of his hunts will increase in direct ratio to his knowledge of the quarry.

From time to time questions regarding ducks have arisen in my mind and puzzled me. I have gleaned the following answers chiefly from books such as those listed in the bibliography. Perhaps some of the same questions have occurred to the reader.

Can a duck smell?

Very slightly, if at all. Smoke in your blinds, light a fire on shore if you wish; it will not interfere with your hunt. Ducks, like all birds, have small nostrils encased in horn. Animals with the keenest sense of smell, such as dogs, deer, and bears, have large nostrils encased in moist flesh. The latter, when hunted, are stalked upwind so the wind is from the quarry to the hunter. Ducks, on the contrary, are usually hunted downwind, the birds thus flying into a wind carrying man's scent. It does not alarm them. Dr. J. C. Phillips writes in his *Natural History of the Ducks:* "There is a deep-rooted conviction among sportsmen that ducks, and particularly mallards and black ducks, have a highly developed sense of smell. All I can say is that I have always sought for evidence on this point and never found any." Dr. C. William Beebe relates that "the question whether vultures foresee their prey by sight or smell has been decided in favor of the former sense. Lacking the ability readily to distinguish delicate odors, we find among birds none of the glands which are so common among hairy-coated creatures."

How about their sense of sight?

It is exquisite! As they can instantly adjust the focus of their eyes from far to near, their power of sight is practically telescopic. Also, a wide iris diaphragm enables them to accommodate themselves better than man to nocturnal conditions. They fly swiftly through trees at night without hitting branches. If a gunner watches live decoys carefully, he notices that they spot approaching ducks before he does. Beebe's opinion is that bird vision "far transcends that of man unaided by artificial aids for scope and delicacy." Vouching for the keen sight of mallards, Phillips noted: "It is evident that when looking straight up they (mallards) can see objects which are invisible to man." It is Thomson's opinion that the telescopic power of a hawk's eyes is so great that, when flying so high as to be almost invisible to man, it can watch prey of its own size running on the ground.

In his interesting book, *The Vertebrate Eye,* Dr. Gordon L. Walls explains the construction and functioning of birds' eyes. Much of the material in the following paragraphs pertaining to the eye has been taken directly from Walls' book, with his permission; and he was good enough to read and check these paragraphs in manuscript.

The importance of eyes to birds, Walls points out, is indicated by the emphasis nature has given them. "The two eyes of a bird often outweigh its brain . . . Hawks and owls, a fraction of the size of man, have eyeballs as large as ours and larger." The eyeballs of a duck occupy a major portion of its head.

A duck's eyes are not "conjugated" like a pair of human eyes. Each is independent of the other in its very limited movements, and in its sensory performance. However, a duck does have a small binocular visual field, in which both eyes see the same things. The eyes are located on the sides of the head, and each has a visual field which exceeds 180° in the horizontal plane and also extends beyond the sagittal plane, overhead, onto the side of the other eye. Where these fields overlap, the duck sees with both eyes—binocularly. It has binocular vision through a narrow angle directly ahead. But this is not all, for since the eyes are near the top of the head there is binocular vision upward also, and even backward. The duck may possibly have stereoscopic (three-dimensional) vision in the binocular areas, but this is not their primary significance—the fields of the two eyes overlap a bit mostly just for insurance against there being too many "blind spots" through which a predator, such as a hawk, could approach unseen.

The duck's "important" seeing is all monocular, whereas ours (or a hawk's) is binocular. The duck sees entirely different sets of objects with his two eyes. If we find it difficult to imagine seeing separate fields with our two eyes, let us remember that we can examine different things simultaneously with our two hands without confusion.

In the retina of each eye the duck has a fovea, a little spot where images are resolved most highly. Since it is about in the center of the retina, the fovea looks straight out from the side of the head. A hawk, on the other hand, has two foveas in each retina, one of which looks sideward while the other looks forward and is used for binocular *foveal* vision—which is impossible for the duck. The duck's acute ability to distinguish motion is largely due simply to its great visual acuity, but it may be enhanced by the pecten, a large pleated fin of pigmented tissue which casts shadows on the retina. It has been claimed that the movements of retinal images over these shadows make their motion more perceptible.

If a hawk circles overhead, a duck usually cants his head and looks skyward with one eye. The purpose of this is to image the hawk on a fovea to see it most clearly. The duck cannot do this, as we can, simply by rolling the eyeball upward in its socket—the eyeball is almost fixed in position. The neck movements by which ducks change their visual fields are facilitated by the great number of neck vertebrae (sixteen, compared with a giraffe's seven!), and by the looseness of their connections. Of birds, Beebe says: "The bones of the neck are all separate and slide back and forth like beads on a string." This flexibility is necessary also for preening, as a duck must be able to reach with its bill the preen gland at the root of the tail, to secure oil to spread on its feathers.

A bird's eye has a third lid, a transparent membrane called the "nictitans," which sweeps sidewise across the eyeball, moistening and protecting it without interfering with vision. Walls notes that "there are many ornithologists who believe that the nictitans is held over the eye most or all of the time that a bird is in the air—the forerunner of the motorcyclist's goggles." In diving ducks, it is also held over the eye while the head is under water, for in these birds the nictitans has a lens built into it which is designed to correct the focus of the eye for underwater vision.

Ducks are not color blind. "No one has ever scientifically questioned that the diurnal birds (birds which are most active in daytime) have color vision." Owls and other nocturnal birds are probably all color blind, seeing the world in daytime in shades of grey, just as we see it by starlight. Walls cites a number of experiments which prove that birds, such as ducks, have about the same kind of color vision as man. Therefore the belief that one should not wear conspicuous colors when duck shooting is well founded!

How about the other senses?

Every gunner knows that a duck's sense of hearing is very acute. But its sense of taste is not supposed to be well developed. That of touch is mostly in the bill, tongue, feet, and flight feathers, the last-named relaying any contact to nerves located in the sheaths.

However, the tonal range audible to birds is not as extensive as that audible

THE VISION OF A DUCK
Areas shown are indicative only.

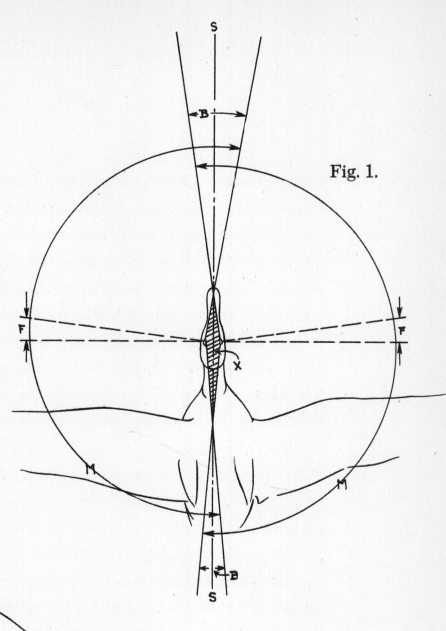

Fig. 1.

Fig. 1. *The Duck's Visual Field in the Horizontal Plane.*

M-M   *Monocular fields.*
B-B   *Binocular fields.*
F-F   *Foveal fields of particularly keen vision.*
X   *Blind field.*
S-S   *Sagittal plane.*

Fig. 2.

Fig. 2. *The Duck's Visual Field in the Frontal Plane.*

M-M   *Monocular fields.*
B-B   *Binocular field.*
F-F   *Foveal fields of particularly keen vision.*
X   *Blind fields.*
S-S   *Sagittal plane.*

to man. At Cornell University, Albert R. Rand, Professor P. Paul Kellog, and Ernest P. Edwards, a graduate student, conducted extensive experiments to ascertain the capacity of birds to hear various tones. Birds were "conditioned" by allowing them to feed only in electrically wired trays. While a bird was feeding a note was struck; immediately afterward the bird was shocked. This procedure was repeated until the bird learned to associate a particular note with an electric shock and jumped whenever the note was sounded. After extensive experiments, it was concluded that normal people can hear higher notes than starlings, which heard the highest notes of any bird tested, and lower notes than a horned owl, which heard lower notes than any other bird tested.*

The only duck experimented with was a canvasback. Edwards reported: "The canvasback, a male, was caught in the wild and tested within a month after its capture. It responded to tones the frequencies of which were 190 to 5200 cycles per second. Thus the lower limit was about half an octave below middle C and the upper limit a few notes above the highest note on the piano."

This is a much narrower range than frequencies of 20 to 16,000 cycles per second heard by the experimenters themselves.

After reading their papers* and believing the "wheeze" of a mallard drake to be a very low frequency indeed, and, hence, that they could hear lower tones than canvasbacks, I took into my blind a pitch pipe, pitched an octave below middle C on the piano. Mallards swimming on the water near the blind evidently heard its note because they stopped swimming and appeared to listen nervously. However, this was too crude an experiment to justify any conclusions.

Dr. Arthur A. Allen, Professor of Ornithology at Cornell University, made an interesting observation: that a ruffed grouse drums with impunity in woods inhabited by the dreaded predator, the horned owl, because the owl cannot hear

*Reported in The Wilson Bulletin, March, 1939, and The Auk, April, 1943.

sounds below 70 cycles a second. The frequency of the drumming sound is only 40 a second. *

Why does a duck require so much food?

Because flight requires large amounts of energy—much more in proportion to weight than land animals require for running and walking. A hummingbird is believed to eat the equivalent of its own weight in food daily. To keep such metabolism going requires high temperature. A duck's normal temperature is 109°F.

Is a red-legged mallard a different species than the yellow-legged mallard?

I have found no satisfactory answer to this. Authorities are divided in their opinions. It is generally assumed that red legs go with larger, heavier bodies, and that this species breeds farther north. I have noticed, however, that the legs of live mallard decoys, which are yellow at the beginning of the season, turn just as red, in the latter part of December and in January when the water is cold, as those of many so-called "ice mallards" of late flights. The decoys' legs turn yellow again in the spring.

How can one tell a black duck drake from a hen?

Because they look so much alike, Jess used to tell me he had never seen a black duck drake. He believed that the drakes took an eastern route to the Gulf and re-joined the hens on their nesting grounds. The contour feathers on the side of the chest of an adult hen show a distinct yellow V. The same feathers on an adult male show a distinct yellow U. The bill of the hen has a greenish tinge; that of the drake tends to an orange-yellow. Incidentally, the U markings disappear in the eclipse plumage.

How can one distinguish a young duck?

Kortright gives an exhaustive list of tests. Most of them are quite technical

* National Geographic Magazine, June, 1945.

and could not be carried out by the average gunner. However, the tail feathers of all adult ducks are pointed. If a tail feather is V-notched or square-ended, it is a juvenile tail feather and the bird is from this year's hatch. The notch is where the juvenile plumes were jointed before they were broken off. In late season, these juvenile tail feathers have been replaced with the first adult winter plumage (See illustration on page 71).

Kortright says: "In species which have bright-colored feet (mallard, black duck, shoveller, and, to a lesser extent, wood duck, blue-winged teal, and gadwall), the foot color of the adult male is usually brighter and more intense than the foot color of the juvenile male in autumn . . . foot color is not a characteristic of age in the female."

Why are so many cripples "winged?"

Nature economizes on the weight of a bird's bones. Its skeleton is light and fragile; most of its largest bones are hollow. A duck's wing bones are fragile, hollow tubes. Upon viewing a broken wing bone, one of my friends exclaimed, "It looks just like a stick of macaroni!" A single shot, even though received at great height, readily fractures any wing bone.

Do ratios of wing areas to bird weights vary?

Yes, very widely. Earl L. Poole compiled an interesting tabulation of such ratios as he found them in a wide variety of North American birds. Together with his observations, it was published in *The Auk,* July 1938.

His tables reveal that the golden-crowned kinglet has seventeen times as much wing area for each gram of body weight as the loon; the black-chinned hummingbird has ten times the area. Summing up his findings among the larger birds he observed that "generally speaking, the owls and the herons possess the highest ratios, with the soaring hawks and the vulture close seconds. There is a decided gap between the latter and the rails. Then follow the fresh-water ducks and geese, the gallinaceous birds, and finally the loons, grebes, and bay ducks."

The ratios he found in ducks compared with a few other examples at both extremes of the scale follow:

Bird	Weight grams	Wing Area sq. cm.	Wing Area per gram
Black-chinned Hummingbird, male	2.55	12.75	5.00
Ruby-throated Hummingbird, male	2.98	12.40	4.16
Eastern Golden-crowned Kinglet	5.75	51.	8.87
American Redstart	8.	62.5	7.61
Green-winged Teal, female	321.	374.	1.16
Blue-winged Teal	332.	370.	1.10
Shoveller	570.	570.	1.00
Wood Duck, male	589.	660.	1.12
Ruddy Duck	635.	394.	.62
Gadwall	723.	718.	.993
Ring-necked Duck	757.31	460.	.61
Lesser Scaup Duck, female	763.	472.	.62
American Pintail	970.	761.	.784
Old-squaw, male	1038.	550.48	.53
Common Black Duck, female	1142.	1007.	.882
Common Mallard, female	1233.5	952.	.769
Common Mallard, male	1408.	1029.	.73
Common Loon, female	2425.	1358.	.56
Common Canada Goose (fat)	5662.	2820.	.498
Whistling Swan	5943.	4156.	.699

What kinds of ducks are there in North America?

The following is a succinct summary of the classification of the American Ornithologists' Union.

River or Pond ducks—*subfamily Anatinae:* Distinguished from diving ducks and mergansers by feeding in shallow water, they "tip up" for food, usually of vegetable origin. Have unlobed hind toes; "fly" out of water.

Mallard	Blue-winged Teal	Gadwall (Grey Duck)
Black Duck	Green-winged Teal	Pintail

Southern Black Duck   New Mexican Duck   Shoveller (Spoonbill)
Baldpate   Florida Duck   Wood Duck
                          Cinnamon Teal

Bay, Sea, or Diving Ducks—*subfamily Nyrocinae:*

Redhead   Eastern Harlequin   Greater and Lesser Scaups
Canvasback   Western Harlequin   Bufflehead
American Golden-eye   American Scoter   Old-squaw
Barrow's Golden-eye   Ring-necked Duck   Eider Ducks
        White-winged Scoter   Surf Scoter

Mergansers—*subfamily Merginae:*

        Hooded Merganser   American Merganser
              Red-breasted Merganser

Ruddy and Masked Ducks—*subfamily Erismaturinae:*

        Ruddy Duck   Masked Duck

Diving ducks, mergansers, and ruddy ducks usually dive for their food, eating, in addition to vegetable foods, mollusk, shell-fish, and fish. Inhabit larger inland waters, deep rivers, and sea coasts. Have large, lobed hind toes to aid swimming; run on water when taking off.

Tree Ducks—*subfamily Dendrocygninae:*

        Black-bellied Tree Duck   Fulvous Tree Duck

Some tree ducks nest in trees, some on the ground. They "tip up" for food like river ducks but also graze on land like geese, with which they form a link to the duck family. Sexes are colored alike.

Coots or so-called mud hens are not of the duck family. They are members of the subfamily Fulicinae of the Rail family, Rallidae. Their feet are not webbed; all toes are lobed individually.

Erect as a West Pointer on parade.

page 251

BIBLIOGRAPHY

Animal Flight. E. H. Hankin. Iliffe & Sons, London, 1913. Contains interesting observations on the flight of soaring birds in India.

The Biology of Birds. John A. Thomson. Macmillan Co., N. Y., 1923. An excellent resumé of the origin, anatomy, life, and habits of all birds.

The Bird. C. William Beebe. Henry Holt & Co., N. Y., 1906. Covers same ground as Thomson. Less technical. Profusely illustrated.

Bird Flight as the Basis of Aviation. Otto Lilienthal. Longmans, Green & Co., N.Y., 1911. An account of this pioneer's observation of bird flight and his attempts to apply it to gliding.

The Book of Bird Life. Arthur A. Allen. D. Van Nostrand, N. Y., 1930. A good, condensed, non-technical resumé of the subject of its title.

Bird Flight. Gordon C. Aymar. Garden City Publishing Co., N. Y., 1938. An excellent, up-to-date, well-illustrated description of bird flight.

Ducks, Geese and Swans of North America. F. H. Kortright. American Wildlife Institute, Washington, D.C., 1942. The best small reference book I know. All North American species described, with methods of identification, succinct life histories, and color plates. Should be in every gunnerman's library.

Encyclopaedia Britannica—Feathers. W. P. Pycraft. This standard reference work, concise and accurate always, contains a good, handy article on the subject.

The Flight of Birds. F. W. Headley. Weatherby & Co., London, 1912. An illuminating discussion of this subject.

Migration of American Birds. Frederick C. Lincoln. Doubleday Doran, N. Y., 1939. Complete, non-technical synopsis of migration. Maps of flyways, etc.

A Natural History of the Ducks (4 Vols.). John C. Phillips. Houghton Mifflin Co., Boston, 1922. The classic of all duck books. Life histories. All species fully described and most of them illustrated in color.

Ornithological Biography (5 Vols.). J. J. Audubon. London, 1833–39. A separate text designed to accompany his famous prints. Contains fascinating observations and accounts of his wanderings. A rare book but found in most good libraries.

Smithsonian Scientific Series—Warm-blooded Vertebrates, Vol. 9. Alexander Wetmore. Smithsonian Institution, Washington, D. C., 1929. A good, short biology by an outstanding authority.

Smoke Streams. C. Townsend Ludington. Coward-McCann, Inc., N.Y., 1943. An excellent, well-illustrated review of the action of air streams on airfoils. Good reference book for anyone interested in flight from either standpoint—birds or airplanes.

The Riddle of Migration. William Rowan. Williams & Wilkins Co., Baltimore, 1931. Deals with interesting theories of migration.

The Vertebrate Eye. Gordon L. Walls. Cranbrook Institute of Science, 1942. Traces the histories, structural patterns, and functioning of vertebrate animals' eyes in a manner which is comprehensible to a layman.

INDEX

Italicized numerals indicate photographs.

Book design and layout by The Illustrators, St. Louis, Mo.

Engraved and printed by The Beck Engraving Company